ALEXANDRE DUMAS, *1802-1870.*

A
GIL BLAS
in California

Los Angeles : The Primavera Press

1933

Introduction

THERE IS *a very considerable element of mystery about* Californie—Un An sur les Bords du San Joaquin et du Sacramento—*Alexandre Dumas' curious book about California during the period of the gold-rush. Few indeed are the tales of the incredible marquis that remain unknown to English-reading peoples, but there are a few, and this is one of them, for it appears in these pages in a complete English version for the first time.*

It seems extraordinary that a story of American life, and especially so competently written a tale of so romantic a period in American expansion as the California gold-rush of '49 should have been 'lost' to American readers so long. But it has been, for since it was published in Brussels in 1852, no English translation of the petit original volume has been discovered, though it was sufficiently popular in Europe three-quarters of a century and more ago, to warrant its publication in German in the same year that the original French edition appeared (1852) under the title Ein Jahr an den Ufern des San Joaquin und des Sacramento, *and a second French edition in 1861, under the altered title,* Un Gil Blas en Californie.

Of Alexandre Dumas (Alexandre Davy de la Paillterie) it may be said as it has been said of Giovanni Jacques Casanova de Seingalt, of Laurence Sterne, of Francois Rabelais and of Thomas Browne, that life gave to him a fair full meed of ex-

[vii]

*perience, and that it owed him nothing on his passing. A pro-
digious worker, he exhibited an enormous capacity for the assi-
milation of pain and pleasure. Both of these he recognized for
the impostors that they are, and in his triumphs over them he
enslaved them and capitalized them in the products of his literary industry.*

*Dumas was born at Villers-Cotterets, July 24, 1802. He
died at Puys, near Dieppe, December 5, 1870. In the sixty-
eight years that intervened he swept forward in the literary
world of two continents with a plangency that was colossal and
a sum total of achievement that was phenomenal. On his death
his published works, all written after 1825, including plays,
novels, travels, essays and memoirs, had attained the amazing
number of 277 volumes.*

Californie *appeared shortly after Dumas had reached the
zenith of his career.* Le Comte de Monte Cristo *was far behind;* Le Vicomte de Bragelonne *was fresh from his fecund
mind; so, too, were* La Tulipe noire *and* Olympe de Clèves.
Ahead were Les Blancs et les Bleus, Les Louves de Machecoul,
*and—his ruinous newspaper ventures in Paris. It was the
period in Dumas' life when he was said to have operated a great
literary factory; to have bought and filched ideas, and hired a
corps of writers to put these ideas into printable shape over his
name.*

Undoubtedly Dumas had many collaborators and Californie,
*strangely, gives credence to the deprecatory, though admittedly
exaggerated, strictures of Querard and others who have sought to
minimize Dumas' accomplishments.*

Californie *purports to be the story of a young Frenchman
who enlisted with his countrymen in a company destined for*

the gold-fields of California. His search for coveted riches was unsuccessful and he returned to France. At Montmorency, a favored holiday retreat of Parisians near Paris where Dumas was visiting, the author and the fortune-seeker met in 1851.

The youth, it developed, had kept a journal of his experiences in California, and this journal, ostensibly, was made the basis of Californie. In the preface to the journal Dumas insists: 'It has been only slightly revised, slightly corrected, and not at all added to by me.' And therein lies mystery.

Disavowing the authorship and yet neglecting to furnish the name of the author, Dumas egregiously proceeds to subscribe himself as the author! Who did write this book, then, the youthful traveler or the elderly author? It is impossible to say with any degree of certainty, though from the internal evidence, and omitting from consideration Dumas' disavowal of authorship, I am inclined to concur in the judgment of the translator, who notes: 'I do feel very definitely the hand of Dumas throughout this record.'

Moreover, there are numerous tricks of the writing trade, known only to professional writers, that have been employed throughout the work, notably a long and extraneous chapter obviously introduced to pad the tale to book-length. The traveler may have been entirely a figment of Dumas' imagination, but it seems more probable that Dumas met him, heard his story, may even have had access to his notes, saw the dramatic possibilities of the tale and composed it immediately.

Californie is entertaining as a tale; it is both entertaining and edifying as a contribution to our understanding of life during the gold-rush. The chapters on market-hunting, living conditions in San Francisco, and mining methods are excellent,

& the story, unlike later reconstructions of the ways of the period by French authors, is remarkably free from factual errors.

To Henry R. Wagner, California bibliophile, historian and geographer, thanks are due for calling this little known item to the attention of the translator—Marguerite Eyer Wilbur—which resulted in its publication in part in Touring Topics during 1931, and to William S. Mason thanks are likewise due for the use of the rare first edition in checking & correlating the two French & the German texts. Californians will be grateful to the translator for making available to them in splendid English an important and delightful book about one of the most romantic periods in the annals of their beloved State.

One may speculate to no end and with little profit on the circumstances surrounding the writing of Californie. One can't help but wonder, at the same time, if it might not have been the subject of numerous reminiscential conversations between Dumas and his last great love—Ada Isaacs Menken—Mazeppa, boasting that she had never 'lived with Houston; it was General Jackson, and Methusaleh, and other big men'—who, from captivating the hearts of California gallants, dashed to the arms of the King of Romance.

PHIL TOWNSEND HANNA.

CONTENTS

CONTENTS

DUMAS TO HIS EDITOR

DUMAS TO HIS
EDITOR

Montmorency
July 20, 1851

My DEAR EDITOR:

YOU WILL no doubt be somewhat surprised, upon glancing down at the end of this letter, to find the signature of a man who is the most prolific writer of books, but the worst letter-writer in the world. This situation will be somewhat clarified when you note that this letter is accompanied by a lengthy manuscript entitled *A year along the banks of the San Joaquín and the Sacramento*. But how, my dear friend, you may perhaps ask, in view of the fact that I met you only eight days ago in Paris, have you been able within these eight days to go to California, remain there a year, and make the return voyage. If you will condescend to read on, this will soon be evident. You know my habits! No one leads a more sedentary life and yet, at the same time, travels more widely. I leave Paris on a trip of three or even four thousand leagues, but remain in my room to turn out from 100 to 150 volumes.

By rare good luck, I decided on the eleventh of last July to go down for two or three days to Enghien. This trip, I may add, was not made, however, purely for pleasure—God forbid that I should indulge in such a luxury! By no means! Desiring rather to recount in my Memoirs a scene that had

taken place at Enghien some twenty-two years ago, I concluded, to avoid error, to revisit certain localities I had not
seen in the interim.

Though aware that at Enghien mineral springs similar to
those found at Pierrefonds and Auteuil had been discovered,
yet I was entirely ignorant of the changes introduced by
this discovery and of the fact that Enghien was on the verge
of becoming a great city such as Geneva, Zurich, or Lucerne,
and was indeed hoping to become a seaport like Asnières.
Accordingly I departed for Enghien by the tram that left
at ten forty-five in the evening. At eleven o'clock I got off
at the station and asked for the road leading from the station over to Enghien. Can you imagine, my good friend, a
Parisian—or what amounts to the same thing, a provincial
who has been living in Paris for the last twenty-five years
—asking at the Enghien station how to reach Enghien!

The result was that the guard whom I asked, believing, I
suppose, that I was merely joking—but which, I can assure
you, was far from my intention—the guard, concealing his
feelings and with the proverbial courtesy of men in public
employ, merely replied, 'Go up as far as the bridge, then
turn to your right.' I thanked him and went on up to the
bridge. Having reached the bridge, I glanced toward the
right and there loomed a city with which I was totally unfamiliar. This, however, was not the Enghien I had known.
What I recalled was an immense marsh entirely covered
with reeds and marshy plants, abounding in duck, sea-divers,
water-fowl, and king-fishers, and with two or three houses
built over it on poles. Such was the Enghien I had known,
the Enghien of my memories, the Enghien where I had gone
hunting twenty-two years ago.

As a result I mistook this conglomeration of houses for another Enghien, and started out to search for the true location. 'Go on,' I had been told, 'as far as the bridge, then turn to the right.' Now on the right was a small inconspicuous road, one used solely by pedestrians. Such a road must surely lead to my old Enghien. I started up this road which led to a field enclosed on all sides by hedges. According to my ideas, while Enghien might not as yet have attained the dignity of a city, yet at least it had not descended to the level of a weed-patch. Enghien was neither Babylon burned by Alexander, nor Carthage destroyed by Scipio. The plow had not passed over Enghien nor had seed been planted in the furrows left by the plow; no evil spell had been cast over this wretched place—so obviously I could not be standing where Enghien had once stood.

I now retraced my steps—that major recourse of travelers who have lost their way and orators who have gone astray in their discourses. I retraced my steps and found, again on my right, a kind of wooden bridge which led me— I was about to say into blackness, but let me correct myself —under a long, dark avenue of trees, through whose foliage I seemed to see, this time on my left, the somber waters of the marsh that moved & caught reflections from the cloudy sky.

Yet the expanse of water at Enghien did not resemble a marsh; however, I was ignorant of the fact that these waters, appreciably diminished, now formed a lake. Accordingly I went boldly along the road knowing, from the moment I saw this body of water, that Enghien could not be far away. The thought that the end of my journey was approaching was entirely agreeable; heavy rains were beginning to descend & I was wearing only light shoes & nankeen trousers. Accelerating my pace, I walked on for perhaps a quarter of an hour. Vague as were my memories, yet the road seemed interminably long and, while I could not understand the absence of houses, yet the constant presence of water on my left reassured me.

Unperturbed by what I saw, I traveled on down the road. A sheltered glade was soon apparent. Hastening on toward this point, I was soon clearly convinced from the local topography that I had mistaken my locations. I had unwittingly been moving around the lake and, having started out from its southern end, had now reached its northern tip.

On the opposite side of this stretch of water gleamed two or three lights indicating the location of the houses for which I had unsuccessfully searched. On my right and left rose— as unexpectedly as theatrical decorations that appear at the sound of a mechanic's whistle—Gothic chateaux, Swiss chalets, Italian villas, and English cottages. On the lake, where duck, sea-divers, coots, mud-hens, and martin-fishers once lived, thousands of white spots shimmered on the waters. These, after a cursory examination, proved to be swans.

You may recall the Parisian who wagered he could walk barefooted over the ice across the great pool of the Tuileries and who, when half way over stopped, saying, 'Upon my word, this is too cold; I prefer to lose my wager!' and retraced his steps. While I failed to follow his example, yet, foolishly or wisely, I continued along the road. Then all the facetious remarks published about me for not having been able to make the tour of the Mediterranean in 1834 came to mind. I imagined what might be written if it became noised abroad that I had not been able to complete the tour of Lake Enghien in 1851; and so, as I have said, I continued on my way.

I followed the circular road that enclosed all this new Venice, aware that by so doing I could not go far astray. To return to my original point of departure was essential and to go back to where I had started I was compelled to pass by the houses built along the causeway which to me constituted the solitary, unique, and true Enghien. Finally, after traveling about a quarter of an hour, I reached the long-anticipated Enghien.

Again I believed I was mistaken, so slightly did this resemble the Enghien of 1827. Finally, from a carriage passing by, I secured information and ascertained that I had now reached my destination. I was directly opposite Hotel Talma. What luck! This would just suit me, for I cherished a strong affection and admiration for this great artist.

Crossing the street, I then knocked at Hotel Talma, where everything was closed, from the vent-hole in the cellar to the loft in the garret. This, however, merely gave me time to philosophize. So it was not true that to forget was universal. For here was a man who, to commemorate Talma, had bestowed on his establishment the name of the revered saint. True, I might have preferred to have seen a monument erected in a village. But, after all, what was I to expect? Far better to have his name, twenty-five years after his death, inscribed on the façade of an hotel rather than not to have his name revered at all.

You are aware, my good friend, how at Westminster the statue of Garrick faces that of King George the Fourth.

There is a certain amount of justice in this, for one was as much king as the other. I decided to put up for the night at Hotel Talma. At first no one answered, so I knocked a second time at the door. A small shutter suddenly flew open, an arm appeared, and a head emerged. This proved to be the head of a man, a head badly tousled, and obviously in an ill- umor; the head of an insolent coachman, or such a head as would grace the conductor of an omnibus. In a word, an insolent head!

'What,' at length asked the head, 'do you want?'

'I want a room, bed, and supper.'

'The hotel is full,' replied the head.

The head then disappeared, the arm pulled in the shutter which was noisily closed, and from behind it the head continued to growl, 'Eleven-thirty—a fine hour to ask for a room and supper!'

'Half-past eleven,' I repeated, 'this seems to me a proper time for supper and bed. But if Hotel Talma is full perhaps I can find something else.'

I now sallied forth resolutely in quest of supper, a room, and a bed. Before me from an immense building streamed brilliant lights and the sound of music. Upon approaching, I read in gilt lettering, Hotel des Quatre-Pavillons. Well, I said to myself, it will be most unfortunate if, under these four flags, there is no room for me. I entered. The ground-floor was brilliantly illuminated; the balance was totally dark. I searched in vain for someone to approach, but here the situation was even worse than in the palace of Beauty in the Woods, where all the world slept. At the Hotel des Quatre-Pavillons, no one, either asleep or awake, could be found. There were only the guests who were dancing, and the musicians who supplied the music. Finally I ventured down the corridor leading to the dancing-salon, where I met someone who appeared to be a servant.

'My good friend,' I asked, 'can I procure supper, a room, and a bed?'

'Where do you want it?' replied the servant.

'Why here, woman!'

'Here?'

'Certainly, am I not in the Hotel des Quatre-Pavillons?'

'Yes, Monsieur.'

'Well, then, have you no rooms?'

'Yes, we shall have more than one hundred and fifty.'

'When will that be?'

'When the hotel is finished.'

'But when will it be finished?'

'As for that, Monsieur, I cannot say. But if Monsieur would care to dance . . .'

I found the 'if Monsieur would care to dance,' of the Hotel des Quatre-Pavillons, almost as impertinent as the 'everything is full,' of Hotel Talma. The result was that I soon left to search for other lodgings.

The only place for which I held out even slight hope was Hotel d'Enghien. The proprietor of a wine-shop that was still open pointed out its location. I went over and knocked, but this time the hotel-keeper did not even bother to reply.

'Well,' said the wine-merchant, shaking his head, 'that is Father Bertrand's custom when there are no vacancies in his hotel.'

'What,' I cried, 'he will not even answer?'

'Why do so,' replied the wine-merchant, 'when accommodations are not available?'

This seemed so logical that I had nothing more to say.
So I dropped my arms and let my head fall on my chest.

'However,' I murmured, 'this is something I could never
have believed possible. No rooms at Enghien!' Then, raising
my head, I observed, 'what about rooms at Montmorency?'

'Ample accommodations.'

'Does old man Leduc still run the Hotel du Cheval Blanc?'

'No, but his son does.'

'Well,' I replied, 'the father was an inn-keeper of the old
school; the son, provided he has studied under his father—
which seems reasonable,—the son must know how to get up
at any hour of the night and find rooms, even when the
house is full.'

And so, accompanied by the same rains which had finally
turned into a steady downpour, I departed for Montmorency.
On the far side of the railroad all seemed natural and un-
changed from what I had known before. This was the same
classic road over which I had travelled twenty years ago,
following walls, crossing fields, passing under the shade of
old walnut trees, and finally entering the village over small,
sharp stones that must have been supplied to the munici-
pality by those who had donkeys for hire in order to impress
on the traveler the impossibility of traveling on foot. I recognized the rapid ascent; I recognized the market-hall; I
recognized the hostelry of Le Cheval Blanc.

The village clock was just striking a quarter past one.
Undaunted, I ventured to knock. What would be said to
me, who, two hours earlier, had been greeted almost like a

vagabond at Hotel Talma? I heard a noise, I saw a light flash, and heard steps resound on the stairs. This time I was not asked what I wanted—the door was opened. There stood a servant half-clad, but pleasant and engaging. She smiled, even though barely awake. Her name was Marguerite. Certain names, my good friend, will remain graven forever in the memory.

'Why Monsieur,' she remarked, 'what a state you are in. In any event you run no risk by coming in, drying off, and changing from wet clothes.'

'As for entering and drying off, I accept from the depths of my heart. But as for other garments . . .'

I showed her the bundle I had been carrying under my arm since alighting from the train and which contained a shirt, two pairs of socks, a chronological manual, and a volume of Michelet's *Revolution*.

'But,' she remarked, 'don't let that distress you; whatever you require will be supplied by Monsieur Leduc.'

Oh saintly hospitality! What makes you supreme and worthy of being revered is not only the fact of being offered without compensation, but also with a friendly voice and a smiling countenance. Saintly hospitality; undoubtedly you dwell at Montmorency; and Rousseau, who was not always entirely judicious, was fully aware of his acts when he asked for hospitality at La Chevrette. I do not know how the poor Marquise d'Espinay received you, sublime author of *Emile;* but certainly she could not have received you, even though knowing you, more graciously than I was received by Marguerite, to whom I was a stranger. Behind Marguerite descended Monsieur Leduc, who at once recognized me.

From then on their hospitality knew no bounds. I was given the finest room in the hotel,—Mademoiselle Rachel's own chamber. Leduc insisted on serving my supper; Marguerite prepared my bed. Under such circumstances I acceded graciously to their every wish. You can readily understand, my good friend, that I had to relate all that had happened & how, at a quarter past one, on foot, drenched to the bones, and with a small bundle under my arm, I happened to knock at the door of Le Cheval Blanc, at Montmorency. Had I come to demand the hospitality of an exile, like Barbaroux or Louvet? Fortunately, I reassured Monsieur Leduc, nothing like this had happened. I had merely come to pass a day or two at Enghien and, not having found supper, a room, or a bed, had pushed on as far as Montmorency. Monsieur Leduc gave a sigh that was far more eloquent in its meaning than the 'Thou, too,' of Cæsar.

I hastened to explain to Monsieur Leduc that I had not come to Enghien for pleasure, but to work. 'Undoubtedly,' replied Monsieur Leduc, 'you can work at Montmorency as well as at Enghien. Here you will be less disturbed.' There was such profound melancholy in these few words, 'You will not be disturbed,' that I hastened at once to reply, 'Yes, and in place of remaining forty-eight hours, I shall remain eight days.'

'And now,' Monsieur Leduc answered, 'if you plan to remain eight days, you can work on something that may surprise you.'

'At what shall I work?'

'On a voyage to California.'

'Come now, dear Monsieur Leduc, don't be foolish!'

'Wait until tomorrow; I will then tell you all about it.'

'Very well; let us wait until tomorrow. Moreover no one in the world is more prone to welcome the unexpected. Once I made a trip to Egypt with Dauzats, but without seeing the country. Find me a man as inspiring as Dauzats, who has just returned from California, & I will return with him.'

'I have just the man for you. A boy arrived today with a complete journal; a boy who is a veritable Gil Blas, a boy who has been in turn a porter, a gold-seeker, who has hunted deer, bear, been an hotel-boy, a wine-merchant, and second in command of the ship on which he returned from San Francisco by way of China, the Straits of Malacca, Bengal, and the Cape of Good Hope.'

'And when can I see him, my good Monsieur Leduc.'

'Whenever you say the word!'

'What I personally find in California,' I went on to say, 'is probably quite different from what others imagine.'

'What do you find there?'

'Oh, that is too long a story for this evening. The hour is now two in the morning. I am quite worn, I have dined well, and I have a good bed. I shall see you tomorrow, Monsieur Leduc.'

The following day Monsieur Leduc brought me his traveler. He was a man twenty-six years old, with an intelligent eye, a black beard, a sympathetic voice, and a skin bronzed by the equatorial suns, for he had recently crossed the equator for the fourth time. Before I had talked with him ten minutes I was convinced that such a man must have kept a most interesting journal. After reading this from beginning to end I was, indeed, aware that my inference had been correct. This is the journal I am now sending you; it has been only slightly revised, corrected, and not at all embellished by my pen.

And may I now tell you personally, my dear editor, what I did not choose to reveal the other evening to Monsieur Leduc about California, giving as an excuse that the hour was too late and we were too tired. What I wished to remark in a general way was what I have discovered on a smaller scale concerning Enghien, which is growing and increasing, whereas Montmorency is weakening and falling into decay. The railroad, that is, civilization, passes only one hundred paces from Enghien, but passes one-half league from Montmorency.

Now, I know a small village in the south called Les Eaux; formerly, that is, about one hundred years ago, this was a prosperous village of men, women and children. It was situated on the side of a hill, in a land rich in fruits, flowers, sweet songs, & refreshing breezes. On Sunday mornings mass was held in a gay little church bright with colored frescoes, before an altar covered with a cloth embroidered by the local women and adorned with small gilded saints made of wood. In the evening dances were held under broad sycamores that sheltered, in addition to the dancers, interested spectators and gay drinkers—three generations of brave men who were born there, who lived there, and who expected to die there. A road passed through the village that ran, I believe, from Tarascon to Nîmes; that is, from one village to another. The life of the small village centered about this road. What, to the province, was merely a secondary outlet was the main artery of this little village, the aorta that caused its very heart to beat. One day, in order to shorten the distance one-half league and travel by perhaps one-half hour, some engineers, unaware that they were plotting murder, mapped out another road. This new road, instead of winding around the mountain, passed through the valley. This left the village off on its left probably less than one-half league away. This, no doubt, seemed of minor importance, but the village now no longer had its road. This road had been its life; its life-force now suddenly ebbed.

The village fell into a decline, sickened, grew seriously ill, and died. I have since seen it dead, entirely dead, devoid of all life. The houses were quite empty, some still closed as they were on the day when those who had lived there went away; in others, open to the four winds, fires had been made on the deserted hearths with broken furniture—perhaps by lost travelers, perhaps by stray Bohemians. The church is still in existence, the checker-like planting of sycamores will remain indefinitely. But the church has lost its songs; the altar cloth hangs in shreds; some wild animal flying perhaps in fright from the church where it had sought refuge has overthrown one of the small wooden saints. The sycamores, too, have lost their musicians, their dancers, their spectators, their drinkers. In the cemetery the father waits in vain for his son; the mother, her daughter; the grandfather, his grandson. In their graves they are astonished not to hear the earth moving around them, and inquire, 'What are they doing up there? Do people no longer die?'

This is exactly what is taking place at Montmorency, which is weakening and languishing, now that the life-giving artery has scorned this place in favor of Enghien. Still at times mistakes are made for all strangers make the pilgrimage to

La Chevrette. Dying, this poor village sees protection only in death. Now genius has this salient benefit—that in the final analysis,it can replace the sun,from whence it emanates. What I have thought, my good friend, is that the progress of civilization is the march of intellectual sunlight. Frequently when I had nothing new or interesting to read I would take out some maps of the world, bound into an immense book comprising endless pages where on each page was contained the record of the rise or fall of some empire. What history was I seeking? The history of the Egyptian, Menes; of the Babylonian, Nimrod; of the Assyrian, Belus; of Phul, of Nineveh; of the Mede,Arbaces; of the Persian,Cambyses; of the Syrian, Rohob; of Scamander, of Troy; of the Lydian, Meon; of Abibal of Tyre; of the Carthaginian, Dido; of the Numidian, Yarbas; of the Sicilian, Gelon; of the Albanian, Romulus; of the Etruscan, Porsena; of the Macedonian, Alexander; of the Roman, Cæsar; of the Frank, Clovis; of the Arabian, Mahomet; of the Teuton, Charlemagne; of the Frenchman, Hughes Capet; of the Florentine Medici; of the Genoan, Columbus; of Charles V of Flanders; of Henry of Gascony; of the Englishman, Newton; of the Muscovite, Pierre VI; of the American, Washington; of the Corsican, Bonaparte? No, not one of these, but rather the universal mother from whom we have all sprung, who has nourished us with her milk, warmed us with her heat—in other words, civilization.

Here is how she accomplishes her vast work which neither straits, mountains, rivers, nor oceans check. Born in the Orient, where day dawns, civilization moves on from India and, leaving behind the ruins of enormous cities which are nothing more than memories, crosses the Straits of Bab el Mandeb, plants on one of the shores Saba, the white, on the other Saba, the black, moves over to the Nile and descends the great Egyptian valley, establishing on the banks of the sacred river, Elephantine, Philæ, Denderah, Thebes, & Memphis. Having reached the mouth of the Euphrates she founds Babylon, Nineveh, Sidon, & Tyre, descends to the sea like the giant Polyphemus &, with her right hand deposits Pergame at the extremity of Africa; with the left Carthage at the tip of Africa; with both hands Athens and Piræus. She then founds twelve great Etruscan cities, baptises Rome, and waits. The first part of her work is accomplished; she has created the great pagan world that begins with Brahma and ends with Cæsar.

A period of tranquility then ensues, an age when Greece gave to the world Homer, Heriod, Orpheus, Æschylus, Sophocles, Euripides, and Plato—an age when the torch was lit. Then, after Rome had conquered Sicily, Africa, Italy, the Pont, the Gauls, Syria, and Egypt, when to speak briefly, she had united them; after Christ, prophesied by Socrates & predicted by Virgil, had been born, this inveterate traveler started again on her journey, dissatisfied until she could return once more to the lands from which she had departed.

Then came the decline of Rome, the downfall of Alexandria, and the loss of Byzantium, which gave way to a second —Carthage, mother of Tunis, to Granada, Seville, Cordova the Arabian Trinity which united Africa and Europe—to Florence and her Medicis from Cosmus the Elder to Cosmus the Tyrant, to Christian Rome with her Julius II, her Leo X, and her Vatican, to Paris with Francis I, Henry IV,

Louis XIV, the Louvre, the Tuileries, and Fontainebleau. These were mutually linked like a group of luminous stars by such men as Saint Augustine, Averroës, Dante, Cimabue, Orcagna, Petrarch, Masaccio, Perugino, Machiavelli, Boccaccio, Raphael, Fra Bartholomeo, Ariosto, Michelangelo, Tasso, Jean de Bologne, Malherbe, Lope de Vega, Calderon, Montaigne, Ronsard, Cervantes, Shakespeare, Corneille, Racine, Molière, Puget, Voltaire, Montesquieu, Rousseau, Goethe, Humboldt, and Chateaubriand. Then civilization, having nothing more to accomplish in Europe, finally crossed the Atlantic as easily as if it were a brook, leading La Fayette to Washington—the old world to the new. Here, where only a few cod-fishermen & fur-traders had been living, she founded, with barely three 3,000,000 inhabitants, a republic that in 60 years increased to 17,000,000 and stretched from the St. Lawrence River to the mouth of the Mississippi, from New York to New Mexico, a land which had the first steamers in 1808, the first locomotive in 1820, a land which produced Franklin and adopted Fulton.

But here, no doubt, she would be embarrassed to continue on her way, for this indefatigable goddess would now have to stop, or turn back, being checked by the double desert dominating the region of the Rocky Mountains. Checked by the Isthmus of Panamá, she could not penetrate into the Pacific except by doubling Cape Horn, & even by making a supreme effort all that would be saved by venturing across the Straits of Magellan would be three or four hundred leagues. And so, for the last sixty years, scholars, geographers, and navigators of all lands have kept their eyes turned toward America. How sacrilegious to believe that to Providence anything is impossible, that obstacles can exist to God!

Here is what happened. A Swiss captain, driven out by the July revolution, traveled from Missouri over to Oregon, and from Oregon to California. Obtaining from the Mexican government a concession of land on the American fork, he was excavating, preparatory to establishing a mill-race, when he saw particles of gold scattered in this soil. This occurred in 1848. In 1848, the white population in California comprised some ten or twelve thousand inhabitants.

Three years have passed by since rumors, emanating from Captain Sutter, were circulated about this gold, rumors which will, in all probability, affect the entire world. California now numbers 200,000 emigrants from all over the world. And, out on the Pacific Ocean, near the most beautiful & the finest gulf in the world, there has arisen a city destined to rival London and Paris.

And so, my good friend, the Rocky Mountains and the Isthmus of Panamá are no more. A railroad will soon run from New York to San Francisco, just as the electric telegraph already connects New York and New Orleans. In place of the Isthmus of Panamá, which is too difficult to pierce, the river Jusgnitto has been utilized and, by cutting through the mountain, a pass will be made from Lake Nicaragua through to the Pacific Ocean.

Moreover, all this is being accomplished at the very time when Abbas Pacho is building a railroad from Suez to El Areich. The result of all this is that a civilization that started out from India has now nearly returned to India and has merely paused for a brief time on the banks of the San Joaquín and Sacramento to ascertain whether, to regain her cradle, she should pass directly across Bering Straits, touchıng with her foot the ruins lying there or wander among the many islands and straits of the inhospitable lands where Cook was assassinated, the abysmal depths that engulfed La Perouse.

In the meanwhile, by utilizing the Suez railroad and route via Nicaragua, within ten years a tour of the world can be made in three months. This is primarily why, my friend, I believe this little volume on California is worth publishing.

Sincerely yours,

ALEXANDRE DUMAS.

A GIL BLAS IN CALIFORNIA

I : THE DEPARTURE

I WAS twenty-four years old and out of work; throughout France the sole topic of conversation at this time was the gold mines of California. On every street corner companies were being organized for the transportation of travelers. These monopolists made ruinous promises regarding what advantages they could offer. I was not rich enough to sit with idle hands; but I was young enough to spend a year or more in an attempt to amass a fortune. So I decided to risk 1,000 francs and my life—the only two things I had wholly at my disposal. Moreover, I was already—as the sailors say—at home on the briny deep. Among my friends was the old man of the sea; by his hand I had been baptized in the tropics when crossing the line. As an apprenticed sailor under Admiral Dupetit-Thouars, I had made the trip out to the Marquesas Islands, had touched on the way out at Point

Teneriffe, Rio de Janeiro, Valparaiso, Tahiti, & Nuka Hiva
and at Woihavo and Lima on the return voyage.*

Having arrived at this decision, there remained merely to
decide which of these societies I should elect to join, a problem fairly difficult of solution. As a matter of fact, I pondered
over this at such length that my choice finally fell on one of
the weakest of these organizations, a company known as the
Société Mutuelle. The headquarters of the Société Mutuelle were at No. 24, Rue Pigale, Paris. Each member joining
was required to contribute 1,000 francs for food & passage.
We were to work together and share equally in all profits.
Furthermore, if one member or partner (which was the same
thing) brought along any goods to sell, the company took
charge of the sale of his wares and guaranteed him one-third
of the profits. In return for the 1,000 francs deposited by
each member the company was to supply, upon our arrival,
lodgings in wooden houses that were carried out with us on
our vessel. Connected with the enterprise were a doctor and
a pharmacist; but each member had to provide himself at
his own expense with a double-barreled gun, using bullets of
a certain size and equipped with bayonet. The pistols could
be of whatever type or size suited the individual purchaser.
Being a hunter I attached considerable importance to this
part of my equipment which, as will be soon apparent, was
indeed fortunate. Upon our arrival we were to work under
leaders whom we selected from our members. Every three

*Captain Abel Dupetit-Thouars left France on the *Venus* in December,
1836, returning in June, 1839. The expedition rounded Cape Horn, visited
the South Seas, Alaska, and California. The record of this trip, *Voyage Au-
tour du Monde*, was published in 1844 in Paris.

months these leaders, who were to work with us and as one of us, were to be changed to avoid dissatisfaction.

Final arrangements were made at Paris, but we were all to congregate at Nantes. At Nantes a ship of some 400 tons was to be purchased through a local banker with whom, according to the company, arrangements had been made in advance. This vessel, moreover, was to take on a cargo—in which we were to share profits—for which the banker was defraying the cost, merely reserving for himself a reasonable percentage of the proceeds. All equipment was being acquired for the Society whose capital was to be reimbursed plus 5 per cent interest. This, obviously, was an extraordinary opportunity—at least on paper.

On May 21, 1849, I departed for Nantes, where I stopped at the Hotel du Commerce. This trip was made with two comrades who had joined this same Society and who were departing at the same time. These two friends were Mr. Mirandole and Mr. Gauthier. Furthermore, another old friend and neighbor from my home town, Tillier of Groslay, had already left ahead of me. We had been companions from early childhood, and his departure had strongly influenced my decision. Tillier had joined the Société Nationale.

At Nantes our troubles began. Owing to certain questions raised between members of the Society and the directors, the banker declined to advance further capital. As a result, the owner who had sold the boat made arrangements for a captain and hired all the sailors, thus being forced to take the entire load on his own shoulders. Since he was in the right and since all his transactions with the Society were perfectly legal, the loss fell on the members themselves, to the amount of some 400 francs each. With the remaining 600 francs the Society was obligated to land us in California. But how? That was the problem! Evidently the Society considered us of minor importance, for we were not consulted in the matter.

The final outcome was that we were loaded into carriages that transported us from Nantes to Laval, from Laval to Mayenne, and from Mayenne to Caen. At Caen we were placed aboard a steamer and brought to Havre. From this port we were scheduled to set sail on July twenty-fifth. But after the twenty-fifth, the twenty-sixth, and the twenty-seventh had come and gone, we grew restive under the absurd excuses offered. Finally, on the twenty-seventh, we were told that we would not be ready to leave before the thirtieth.

For three days we waited patiently in the interests of our company. By recalling how, in February, 1848, workers had spent three miserable months in the service of our country, we concluded that by comparison what we were enduring was of minor importance. So we resigned ourselves to the delay.

But, unfortunately, on July thirtieth another statement was given out—the date of departure had been moved ahead to August twentieth. The poorest members of our party talked of a revolt not knowing, in fact, how they were to live during these twenty-one days. But rich shared with poor— & we awaited the twentieth of August. But on the very eve of our departure we made a new discovery; namely, that the Society being, or pretending to be, even poorer than its members, would be unable to provide many things of primary importance for a voyage such as we were about to undertake.

These articles were sugar, coffee, rum, tea, and brandy. We voiced our protests; we made angry remarks; we even renewed our threats to bring suit—but the company was obdurate. And so the unfortunate members of the Society were forced to dig down to the depths of their pockets. Unluckily, many proved so deep that the bottom could not be reached. Finally a supply of these vitally important commodities was provided for common use, mutual promises being exchanged to use the utmost moderation with these luxuries.

The day of our departure at length dawned. Our ship was the *Cachalot*,* an old whaling vessel, that was reputed furthermore to be one of the finest vessels afloat. She was a boat of 500 tons. During the two days prior to our departure crowds of relatives came down to Havre to see us off. Among them were many mothers and sisters who were extremely devout, and inasmuch as only a few of the travelers were atheists, and this was our last day before leaving on a voyage of six months' duration, a journey that was to take us from the Atlantic on over into Pacific waters, the decision was reached to make one final expenditure to hold mass on behalf of a safe journey. Arrangements were accordingly made for a special mass to be held in the church.

Mass said on the eve of such a departure is invariably a grave affair; for some who participated, this would undoubtedly be their last mass. Such was the comment made to me by a delightful youth nearby who was listening devoutly to this mass; he was one of the editors of the *Journal du Commerce*, and was called Bottin. I silently indicated by nodding my head that I was thinking at that same moment exactly what he had just voiced. During the elevation of the host,

*Spermaceti—whale.

I glanced around; everyone was kneeling and, I can assure you, all were praying devoutly.

When mass was over, a proposal was made to hold a fraternal banquet at a cost of one franc, fifty centimes each.* We numbered 150 passengers all told, 15 of whom were women. By turning our pockets inside, 225 francs were finally collected. This sum was adequate. This last dissipation, however, made sad inroads into what remained of our capital. That our parents and friends were forced to contribute on their own behalf goes without saying, for we were not rich enough to include them. Mirandole and two others were appointed a committee of three & arranged at a price of thirty sous, a splendid banquet despite our meager capital.

The banquet was to take place at Ingouville; at four o'clock we were all to assemble at the docks and at five o'clock take our places at the banquet table. All were as punctual as if attending mass. Since the participants arrived in pairs, they were seated in an orderly manner. An effort was made to be gay. I say an effort was made; for, as a matter of fact, everyone was sad at heart, and I strongly suspect that the more noise they made the more profound was their inward grief.

Toasts were offered for a safe journey; wishes were extended for finding the richest placers on the San Joaquín; the thickest lodes on the Sacramento. The master-owner of the *Cachalot*, furthermore, was not neglected. For in addition to his quota of one franc, fifty centimes, he had actually sent over two hampers of champagne. The banquet was prolonged far into the night. Then as our heads grew light we attained something approximating gayety.

*Approximately 30 cents; the franc was worth 20 cents, and contained 100 centimes.

The following day in the early hours of the morning the sailors in turn paraded through the city carrying flags and bouquets. This parade terminated at the port where the entire population had assembled to see us off and bid us farewell. Everyone moved hastily from shop to shop. Not until the moment of departure had actually arrived were we aware of what we might need after we had departed. I, for my part, laid in a supply of powder and balls; ten pounds of one and forty pounds of the other.

At eleven o'clock the ship pulled out of port, sped by a pleasant little northwest breeze. Ahead of us was an American boat being towed by the steamer *Le Mercure*. We moved out from the jetty singing the *Marseillaise, Chant du Départ*, and *Mourir pour la Patrie*. Handkerchiefs fluttered en masse from the docks; handkerchiefs fluttered en masse from our ship. A few relatives and friends had come aboard ship with us. Halfway out in the harbor the pilot and owner returned, relatives and friends returning with them. This was a second farewell, a farewell far more gloomy than the first. Those who had set out to seek their fortunes were now finally left alone. The women wept; the men perhaps wished they were women and could weep. So long as land remained in sight, all eyes were turned toward land. That evening on toward five o'clock this finally vanished, not to be sighted again until Cape Horn was reached at the remote tip of another world.

II : FROM HAVRE TO VALPARAISO

ON BOARD, as I have said, were fifty passengers; of this number fifteen were women, two being in the captain's rooms and the others housed down below. The crew consisted of a captain, a second officer, a lieutenant, eight men, and a cabin-boy. The spar-deck, being reserved for passengers, had not been loaded with merchandise; this had been planned for the accommodation of travelers, and contained four rows of cabins. We were two in a cabin, one bunk being over the other. Mr. de Mirandole was my cabin-mate. The women had separate quarters; a kind of open space had been constructed for them to the rear of larboard.

Our 150 passengers comprised members sent out by three companies; no one received what quarters he had engaged—

even though he had scrupulously paid for them in cash. The result was that there was scarcely room enough for the passengers, and absolutely no space available for our trunks. So everyone had his luggage out in front of his cabin on deck; this served not only as a place to sit but also as a toilet table. Any other superfluous baggage was stowed away down in the hold. What space remained aboard ship was given over to merchandise belonging both to owner and passengers. This merchandise consisted of alcohol and hardware.

Our first dinner on board ship was served at five o'clock, just as land disappeared behind the horizon. So far no one was seasick, but no one had much appetite. The table was placed on deck, or rather the deck was used for a table. The ship being overcrowded, the deck was cluttered with cases of sulphuric acid, kegs of water for use during the passage, and planks cut ready to be erected and made into houses upon our arrival. In addition, we carried a dozen small houses that were already built and were no more trouble to erect than to assemble a clock. These had been built at Havre and sold for 100 up to 125 francs.

The first day, as is customary soon after leaving port, dinner consisted of soup, some boiled meat, a quart of wine, and an extremely small portion of bread. This at once led us to believe that bread was not abundant on board. As a matter of fact, later on we had bread only on Sundays and Thursdays; on other days we ate biscuits. For every eight passengers there was a large tin bowl; into this each one dipped with his plate, which was his complete table service. We squatted down like Orientals and ate in this fashion. That same day on toward eight o'clock in the evening, we fell in

with some south winds. These continued to blow throughout the night and by the following day were violent enough
to carry us off the English coast. Here a fisherman came
aboard; his boat was full of fish. After some bargaining he
took off our mail.

One of the crying needs of man who travels far, traverses
a vast expanse of water, and finds himself surrounded solely
by sky and water, is the need to send back news to those
from whom he has just parted. He feels so minute in this vast
stretch of universe that by binding himself by means of a
letter to land he affords himself the consolation of feeling
that he is not utterly lost. Unfortunate indeed are those who,
under these conditions, have no one to whom to write! The
fisherman went off loaded down like a postman with mail.

The evening of our second day out the winds again veered
without having caused the loss of much time, or proven weari-
some. From then on we made steady headway. The captain
who, as has been said, was quite parsimonious, owing to the
small amount of wheat carried aboard, with bread, had placat-
ed us by saying that we were to put in at Madeira and take
on potatoes. The winds, however, being favorable, from the
standpoint of economy of time it seemed wiser at the last
moment to continue directly on our course. Yet we did not
fail to make several pointed remarks that led him to understand that we were not blind to the economies he was prac-
tising on us. A captain, however, is king on board his vessel.
Though we were in the majority, yet he decided that we
should continue on our route & that a favorable wind would
have to act as substitute for potatoes. As a matter of fact,
we all rejoiced at moving steadily ahead. The *Cachalot*, as

has been said, was a good sailor and even on poor days we still made six or seven knots per hour.

Off Senegal our watch sighted a ship; she proved to be an American frigate out cruising. Altering her course she came up to us, dipping her colors. We did the same, exchanged latitudes and longitudes—the good-morning and good-evening of sailors—then continued on our route, while the frigate proceeded on her journey. To us these exchanges of latitude and longitude had a certain definite value for we had on board quite a poor chronometer. Even the name of the frigate that had just rendered this service was unknown to us; except for a flamboyant band, indicating her guns, she was painted entirely black, like the ship of the Red Corsair.

As we proceeded further on toward the equator, definite signs of this region began to appear. The waters of the sea turned a deeper blue; large banks of weeds called tropical raisins were encountered; flying fish skimmed the waters; schools of bonito and dorado passed by; the heat grew oppressive, all unfailing indications. Fishing for bonito and dorado now began. Such fishing becomes extremely simple and easy by making use of what has been devised by venerable fishermen along the banks of the Seine. This is the fishing art in its infancy. Over the bowsprit a certain number of cords are hung, on whose ends are tied what resemble flying fish. The pitching of the ship plunges the bait in and out of the water and so each time the strings leave the water, dorado and bonito, mistaking the bait for live fish, jump for it and are caught on the hook. This is a veritable manna that God sends in this warm latitude to us poor passengers.

The fishing was universal. At length we reached & crossed

the line. Needless to say, in honor of this solemn occasion all the customary ceremonies were held; for the ladies was devised a very gallant Neptune, of extremely venerable appearance; an Amphitrite, who makes alluring advances to men; and some Tritons who soused us with endless buckets of salt-water. Naturally, in my capacity of seasoned traveler, I had already had the sun before and behind me and so I could participate in this pageant from the spectators' gallery, in other words, from the crow's-nest.

Having already referred to the women, I shall now speak of them again. Those on board were not, as can be readily understood, religiously inclined; as a result when our boat was well under way in addition to lotto, dominoes, backgammon, and écarté, they played another game called marriage, which consisted in its two salient aspects of being married and being divorced. Inasmuch as there were only 15 women and 135 men on our vessel this was more than a game; it was almost an institution—a philanthropic institution. Of the fifteen women, three were already engaged prior to our departure. All three had genuine husbands, or rather genuine lovers, and consequently if they married it was merely a mock marriage. Each one of these marriages was attended by functions corresponding to those fulfilled by witnesses, relatives, or priests in serious marriages. These duties were executed with the utmost gravity.

Another serious task requiring absolute impartiality had also been devised. This was the task of acting as judge. Here is a typical instance. One of our friends, B—, had brought his mistress with him. Before leaving France he had made, at considerable personal sacrifice, a heavy purchase of dresses of silk, wool, and poplin, large and small shawls, hats, etc. But it so happened on the trip that, by one of those caprices that invariably occur on voyages, Mlle. X— found M. D— preferable to her former companion whom she now left.

In addition to the complaints and recriminations of her former friend who was of the belief that if he had lost his hold over her he might at least retain her personal effects, he promptly seized all her wardrobe one morning, leaving only one garment. Warm though it was at the equator where the event occurred, what she retained was quite inadequate. So the victim voiced her complaints and in the meanwhile called on us for assistance. Although we may have felt that the single garment suited Mlle. X— to perfection, yet we were too fair-minded not to respond to her appeal. A tribunal was arranged, & judges appointed. From this arose the founding of this new office. These intermediaries handed down a decision which, in my opinion, rivaled the judgment of Solomon.

Their decision ran as follows: First, that Mlle. X— had the right to bestow her affections as she desired & preferred. Second, that she could not justly be deprived of clothing, and that Juno alone had the right to appear

> *In the simple garment*
> *Of beauty recently aroused from sleep*

and as a result B— would be required to return to her what she needed, that is, her lingerie, stockings, two dresses, a hat, and a bonnet. Third, all other garments, being deemed superfluous, were to be retained by B—. This decision was rendered to B— with all the customary formalities and, since he had no appeal, he was forced to submit without redress. So Mlle. X— brought by way of dot to her new husband only the barest necessities which D—circumvented by presenting to her his own dressing-robe from which she made a dress, and a cover from which she made a wrap. Mlle. X—, it must be said, looked charming in this new costume.

Our voyage continued with favorable winds. Time and again we were within sight of the Brazilian coast. We came close to land near Montevideo, and saw from afar this second Troy, besieged for the last eight years. The most delicate, those who had suffered the most upon leaving, now began to grow accustomed to the sea and, despite all the minor inconveniences inevitable on such a journey, our voyage proved quite gay. And why should we be sad? Had not each of us elected to pursue the golden phantom called fortune? During the day, time hung somewhat heavy on our hands, but at night all passengers came up on deck, for to attempt to sleep down below was equivalent to being asphyxiated.

Up on deck Bottin regaled us with stories. As I have already said, he had a charming personality & everyone liked him as much for his egotism as for the pleasure he gave. In addition to his talents as story-teller and historian, Bottin was a poet and had even composed songs which were sung to us by a student from the conservatory, Hennecart by name, who was an excellent musician with a fine voice. After reaching San Francisco he gave several evening concerts that met with signal success at the French theatre on Washington Street. But after fire destroyed the theatre, the actors left for the mines and Hennecart found a place at a café called The Independence, where he sang for 500 francs a week, or slightly more than 2,000 francs a month. But for a time Hennecart sang aboard our whaler on Ocean Street.

Twice a week, on Thursdays and Sundays, a ball was held. A section of the deck, which upon departure was crowded with kegs holding water, was automatically cleared as the water was consumed and this afforded deck-space to dance. A German played the cornet and a Frenchman the fife. The two instruments and these two musicians comprised our entire orchestra, but this did not deter us from dancing the various national dances of France with all the animation at our command.

With dancing and singing up on deck, our ship reached Cape Horn. There, through dense fog, Tierra del Fuego was sighted. The winds were favorable and we skirted the shores at such close range that in the open spaces great water birds were seen walking along the shore. These creatures stopped to watch us, standing motionless on their long legs.

We killed many petrel and albatross, catching some by fishing, which was far more economical, for in place of using powder and lead, as in hunting, the fishing required only a small piece of pork. This bait was attached to a hook and suspended on the end of a cord. The petrel and albatross seized this bit of pork with their usual gluttony and were thus trapped by the hook. Then they were caught, knocked down, dressed, and soaked in brandy. By some rare culinary art our master cook succeeded in disguising the taste of the game until it was edible. Fishing for albatross and petrel replaced in these waters our zealous angling for bonito and dorado in the tropics.

Idly fishing and hunting, we were rounding the cape between land and rocks when suddenly, about nine o'clock one night, the wind that had been favorable veered abruptly and began blowing with considerable force. Now we had known in advance of this bad passage that lies at the tip of the cape famed for its tempests,& the haunt of the giant Adamastor.* But we had been so fortunate until then that we hoped to slip through while Adamastor was not watching.

Our hopes were frustrated; the giant saw us, inflated his chest, and began to blow. His breath strongly resembled a tempest. We were now forced to reef the royal mast top-sails, haul in the main-sail and proceed carrying only the fore-sail, top-sail, & the small jib. But within an hour we were forced to take in reefs. Then, as the storm gained in force, we took in all but the small jib & the large top-sail, both fully reefed, Ten minutes later we were at the full mercy of the seas, and riding before the gale.

The passengers up on deck began to lose courage and demand to be allowed to go below. Even if they had not made this request, the order would undoubtedly have been issued, for in bad weather nothing annoys the sailors so much as the passengers.

Three-quarters of the passengers had gone below when a violent wave from starboard broke open the hatches. The waves that had been anticipating just this calamity came in through this opening, and in less than ten minutes two feet of water poured in below decks. The trunks now began to

---

*According to legend, Adamastor appeared at night when the fleet of Vasco da Gama was nearing the Cape of Good Hope, and warned the vessels not to pass his domains. Since then his name has been synonymous with a stormy cape.

float—invariably an ominous sign—for the top of the hatch had been entirely carried off by the force of the water.

The hatch was covered over. Then the pumps were started. This time the passengers did not wait for orders to go up on deck. When they felt the water around their knees, when they saw the trunks, valises, and boxes begin to dance, they scrambled up the ladders, leaving the hatches even more quickly than they had been engulfed.

The captain called all hands to man the pumps. The situation was critical & every man aboard responded with every ounce of his strength to the task. Everyone seemed to feel that his neighbor was too weak to work, & insisted on taking a turn. The women were somewhat frightened at first, but when they found they were not drowned they came back laughing through the water to encourage us. Night, an intensely black night, was passed in the same way, that is, hanging between life and death, probably a little nearer death than life. Day finally broke, and with the dawn an east wind returned.

Damages having been repaired, our ship tranquilly resumed her course and by traveling at ten knots made up what time had been lost during the night. Upon rounding the cape we sighted a three-master; however she was too far away for us to be able to recognize either her build or her flag. At length we passed out into the Pacific Ocean which was recognized from afar by its waves. From now on fine weather and favorable winds lasted until we arrived at Valparaiso.

III : VALPARAISO TO SAN FRANCISCO

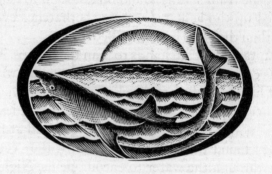

FIFTEEN DAYS before reaching Valparaiso our supply of potatoes ran out. This shortage was seriously felt. For them had been substituted a concoction of wheat, brandy, and molasses. The eight comrades who shared the same tin dish pooled their rations and made a plum-pudding, which was cooked in sacks in boiling water. But ingenious as man may be, potatoes do not take the place of bread; neither does plum-pudding replace potatoes. Valparaiso now seemed to us like the promised land; among every little group was heard only the word: Valparaiso, Valparaiso! Three months had already been spent on the water, and with Valparaiso once passed, only one-quarter of our journey remained. The remaining three-quarters was behind us, forgotten, vanished, utterly obliterated by tempests around Cape Horn.

Finally one Tuesday from the crow's nest was heard the cry of 'Land, land.' Each passenger at once verified the truth of this report with his own eyes, then hastened to put on his best clothes, preparatory to landing, and to check over his accounts to find out exactly how much he had left to spend. Anchor was cast in the main roadstead—that is, some three-quarters of a league off shore. Soon, leaving Valparaiso with as much zeal as if competing for regatta prizes, were seen a dozen small boats known as whale-boats. Within fifteen minutes these boats were swarming about our ship. At the first mention of price by the Chilians who manned these boats, we recognized the crass absurdity of their demands. They could not, so they said, land us for less than thirty-six sous each,—three reales in Chilian currency.* Obviously such a sum was prohibitive to men who had passed through the hands of Californian companies, who had been stranded at Nantes, remaining there fifteen days, who from Nantes had been sent to Havre, and who had remained six weeks in Havre. At this price half of us might perhaps have been able to land, but one-half of this half could not have returned to their vessel.

Having keenly argued in behalf of our interests, we finally fixed the price at one real. Moreover, under these trying circumstances the brotherly spirit on board showed itself at its finest and best. Those who had money looked at the money in their hands & then smilingly held out their hands to their comrades. Those who were short the full amount, or those who had nothing, came over & helped themselves from the hands extended by their friends. The price having been fixed and all now having the amount required to go ashore, pass thirty-six hours on land, and return, we all jumped quickly down into

*The sou, or halfpenny.

the boats & within fifteen minutes were ashore. By this time it was four o'clock in the afternoon. Once ashore we all scattered, everyone seeking what adventures appealed most strongly, or what especially fitted the size of his purse. Although my purse was not heavy, yet it was adequate. Moreover, I had acquired experience from my former voyage, for in going out to the Marquesas Islands with Admiral Dupetit-Thouars, I had previously touched at Valparaiso. I was somewhat familiar, in consequence, with the country.

Mirandole, who was aware of my past experiences, put himself in my charge and refused to leave me. So we went over to the Hotel du Commerce. As it was now five o'clock and there was not much to be done that day, we decided to visit the theatre, a magnificent building that had been put up since my last voyage. This was situated on one of the four sides of the plaza which, if not the most beautiful, is, with its central fountain and its grove of orange-trees as dense as an oak grove and full of golden fruits, at least one of the most delightful places in the world. In this place, with no other distractions than our day-dreams, refreshed by the evening wind, and inhaling the fragrant odor of oranges, we spent two of the most enjoyable hours of our lives. Our companions had scattered, however, like so many school-boys out on a holiday, rushing from Fortop to Maintop. But what are Fortop & Maintop? From what are these strange names derived? I know nothing definite about them so I shall confine myself to answering the first question. Fortop & Maintop are two public dance-halls behind which the hills of Mabrille and Chaumière rise. Fortop and Maintop are to Valparaiso what music-halls are to Amsterdam & the Hague.

Here are to be found handsome Chilian women with olive complexions, large well-formed black eyes, shapely temples, and sleek, glossy-black hair, who are clad in bright-colored silks cut décolleté down to the waist. Here polkas & *chillas*, (which are practically unknown in France) are danced to the accompaniment of guitars and singing, punctuated by blows struck with the palm of the hand on tables. Here, too, occur brief quarrels followed by lasting revenge. Here are spoken words that bring on duels that are fought out with the knife.

The night was passed waiting for day to dawn. The delights of the dance were superseded, the following morning, by the delights of riding. The Frenchman, especially the Parisian, is a born horseman; he has made a study of this art and has practiced on the donkeys of mother Champaign at Montmorency, and on the horses of Ravelet, at Saint Germain. The captain, in giving us shore leave on Tuesday evening, had warned the passengers to be ready to depart the following Thursday. The signal for returning was to be the tri-colored French flag and the red flag flying at the foremast. Five hours would still remain from the time the red flag was hoisted aloft. But it was not until Thursday morning that it would be necessary to watch anxiously for the red or tri-colored flag. Wednesday was entirely our own, from one evening to the next, a full twenty-four hours; in other words, a moment or an eternity based on whether pleasure or grief marks the passing of time.

Our main amusement for that day was to be a ride along the Santiago road, running from Valparaiso over to Avigny. Those who did not have funds enough to hire horses remained behind in the city. I was among those spendthrifts who, disregarding the future, spent their last reales for this joyous trip. Why, moreover, be perturbed? To think only of the future would be futile; three-fourths of the trip was now past; only five weeks more traveling remained and our goal would be reached—our goal, the placers of the San Joaquín and the Sacramento.

Along the road we saw grotesque clowns, mounted on horses like the pygmies of German and Scotch ballads, pass at close range. These proved to be magnificent Chilian riders wearing trousers split, buttoned, & embroidered from where the leather is split down to the end of the boot and worn over other trousers of silk, small round vests, elegant ponchos, broad-brimmed, pointed hats, trimmed with silver galloon on their heads, carrying lassos in their hands, and sabers and pistols in their belts. All were traveling along at a lively gallop in saddles embroidered in striking colors, on which they held their seats as firmly as if in arm-chairs.

The trip soon came to an end. We had the appearance, in our impatience to be on the move, of attempting to outride time; and yet, without losing a moment, these indifferent hours moved on in their customary way. In the morning our horses were fresh and in good wind; during the middle of the day they were panting and subdued; in the evening they were sad and dejected.

The women who accompanied us everywhere were even more enthusiastic, more adventuresome, and more indefatigable than the men. Bottin was fairly bursting with energy, jokes, and gayety. Forming into small groups, we went in for dinner. Wherever a man travels with a party, he has his own circle of friends, those toward whom he is lukewarm, and his enemies.

The following day, Thursday, by eight o'clock in the morning everyone was down at the docks. There we saw the red flag, and were informed that it had been up approximately two hours. Three hours still remained. Only three more hours; how quickly these pass for travelers who have but three hours more on shore. Each of us utilized to the full these three hours. Those who had funds left seized this chance to lay in a supply of what the Chilians call fruit-bread. This bread made of fruits is, as the name indicates, a concoction of dried fruits. These when sold are cut into thin slices, and have the shape of a round cheese.

At ten-thirty we hired for one real the same boats that had taken our party ashore. Our group was now taken back to the ship and, upon arriving, each one reinstated himself in his or her corner. Precisely at two o'clock anchor was hoisted and sail raised; the wind was perfect. By dusk, land had dropped from sight. Ahead of us were a Sardinian brig and an English three-master which we rapidly outdistanced. We left behind lying at anchor the French frigate L'Algérie; she had one of our sailors aboard who had been placed there in service, owing to some trouble he had had with an officer.

Since few persons understand this essentially maritime expression, 'placed in service,' a brief explanation will be given. When a sailor proves unruly aboard a merchant vessel, if the captain meets a warship and if he wishes to get rid of a sailor, he 'places' him in service. In other words, any sailor whom he refuses to keep because of incorrigibility can be turned over to the government. The sailor thus passes, at the whim of the captain, from a merchant ship over to the navy. This, it must be conceded, is an unfortunate way of securing recruits for the navy; for soldiers ashore special companies have been formed for disciplinary purposes. Furthermore, frequently captains who do not have to account to anyone for their acts and conduct are flagrantly unjust to certain poor devils toward whom they have conceived a dislike and whom they get rid of in this fashion. I have cause to suspect, for instance, that our poor sailor may have fallen a victim to the ill-humor of our own captain.

The breeze was strong and the sea rough and, as we had spent forty hours ashore, seasickness now overtook those least acclimated to the pitching of our vessel. The women in general—and I, in turn, must repeat the same remark that others have made before me—the women endured this long and tiresome voyage far better than the men. Up until that time, oddly enough, we had not had among our 150 passengers aboard, a single case of sickness, nor even an accident. From this fortunate situation, however, we were soon cruelly to be awakened. We had just passed Panamá, crossed the line in the opposite direction from which we had passed before, and were sailing ahead under a mild breeze with all sails set, even to the studding-sails, but actually, as a matter of fact, not traveling over four or five knots an hour—which was quite remarkable considering the calms usually experienced out in these waters—when suddenly near the seventeenth parallel was heard the hideous cry, 'Man overboard!'

On warships provision is made for just such emergencies. Buoys are provided and a man is always ready to handle the pulleys of the small boats, which have only to be lowered by their ropes. So, provided the water is not rough, or a man does not know how to swim, only in rare instances is there not time enough to save him. But this situation does not hold true of merchant vessels, with their crews of only eight or ten men, and the boats in use up on deck. At the cry of 'man overboard,' while our members were looking around, counting faces, and searching anxiously to find out who was missing, I climbed rapidly into the crow's-nest. My eyes followed the trail in the wake of our ship where among the foam, and already more than 150 feet away, I recognized Bottin.

'Bottin's fallen in,' I called.

Now Bottin was so generally beloved that at his name I am certain everyone put forth added energy. By this time one of the main yards had already been hurled in off the stern of the vessel. Bottin had been washing his clothes—we were all, as can be readily understood, our own laundrymen—and had decided to dry his linen out on the shrouds. In so doing his foot had slipped, and he had fallen unobserved into the ocean. Upon hearing his one cry the helmsman had looked back and observing a man appear in the wake of the vessel had, without knowing who this man was, uttered the cry that had struck terror to our hearts, the cry, 'Man overboard!'

I was not mistaken. At the words, 'It's Bottin!' captain & passengers realized that they must immediately unfasten the yawl which was now lowered over the deck into the water. An officer and an assistant flung themselves—how I do not know—into the yawl. Simultaneously, the captain ordered the ship to be brought about, allowing the three sails to remain flapping idly.

Under these conditions the accident should not have been very serious; the weather was superb and Bottin an excellent swimmer. When he saw the yawl lowered into the water he signalled with his arm to indicate that haste was unnecessary. Although he was swimming toward the main-top-gallant yard he was obviously swimming this way merely because it was on his course and not because he needed this yard for support. The yawl, manned by the officer and the sailor, rowed, however, rapidly toward the swimmer. From the mizzen-top I was watching the distance between Bottin and the boat diminish. Bottin was constantly making reassuring signs to us; in fact the boat was only about 150 paces away from him when I suddenly saw him disappear.

At first I believed a wave had covered him and that, once the wave had passed, he would reappear. The two men in the boat shared my belief for they continued to row ahead. But after a short time I saw them stop, look anxiously around, stand up, shield their eyes with their hands, search everywhere, turn in our direction as if to consult us, then again scan the boundless depths. The expanse of the sea was unbroken; nothing reappeared. Our poor friend Bottin must have been snatched by a shark.

Of the nature of his death there was little room for doubt. He was far too good a swimmer to disappear so suddenly. Even men who do not know how to swim come up twice or three times before finally sinking. For over two hours a search was made near where he had last been seen. The captain could not bring himself to recall the yawl; the lieutenant and the seaman were reluctant to return. At length it seemed advisable to proceed on our journey; the signal of recall was given, and the yawl came sadly back, towing in the yard-arm that she had in the meanwhile rescued. There was heavy

mourning on board our vessel. Bottin was universally popular and had been the leading mediator in all our quarrels.
The death of our unfortunate friend was now legally certi-
fied and his personal belongings and papers entrusted to the
captain. These effects, fifteen days after his death, were sold
at auction, his papers being reserved to be sent on to his
family. There was no more singing at night; the next Sunday
there was no dancing. We were all depressed. Gradually,
however, we resumed our usual mode of life; but now and
then during the course of conversations would recur the
words, 'Poor old Bottin!'

IV: SAN FRANCISCO

ON JANUARY 5, 1850, despite a heavy fog a sailor who was engaged in furling a sail cried, 'Land!' Throughout the sixth, however, a futile search was made for the bay, which had been passed. Not until the morning of the seventh was its entrance finally located. But during the sixth the fog lifted, enabling us to form some idea of the aspect of the country.

The land appeared to rise gently in the form of an amphitheatre. On its first level were visible herds of deer and cattle grazing peacefully in fields of emerald-like greenness. They seemed as unperturbed as if the world had just been created. On the lowest level were grass and pastures, but no trees; on the second appeared firs of great height and thickness and, here and there, groups of hazelnut and laurel trees. Over the third towered the crests of mountains, culminating in the lofty peak known as Mt. Diablo. The nearer we approached the bay on the sixth, the scarcer grew the trees, while its rocks, like the sharp bones of some huge skeleton, began to stand out in considerable number among the verdure.

We now put out to sea in order to pass a restful night, for we were so surrounded by ships led astray, like ourselves, and also searching for the bay that there was danger of running afoul after dark. Though remote from danger of collision, yet we did not fail to hang a ship's lantern out on the end of the flying-jib. We were at peace with the world—a peace marked by graveness and contentment—for the world that we were about to enter was a totally foreign world. At Valparaiso we had secured a certain amount of information that was vague because of its remoteness,—in other words, what information we received was both favorable & unfavorable.

On the morning of the seventh, preparations to disembark were made. No longer, as at Valparaiso, did we plan to seek in the city a few hours of capricious distractions or foolish pleasures, we were about to seek work, and—what is the rarest thing in the world—remuneration for our labor. So the calmest man among us would have lied had he said that he slept soundly. I, for my part, awoke ten times or more during the night. On the seventh, long before daybreak, everyone was up on deck.

When the sun rose we could see land, but this was still so remote that the entrance to the bay was not even visible. From five o'clock in the morning until noon, we ran before a quartering wind. Not until noon were the head lands that formed its opening for the first time faintly visible. On the right side of the bay appeared two rocks, cut through at their base but connected on top, a formation that had created an arch. All along the shores glistened sand, white as silver-dust. Only at Fort Williams did the greenness begin to appear.* On the left rose mountains that were rocky at their base but green one-third of the way up their slopes. On these mountains herds of cattle grazed.

Soon our attention was diverted from the left coast, where there was only, as at Sauroleta, a small bay where a few ships rode at anchor, and centered on the right side. We were now approaching Fort Williams. Having passed Fort Williams, two islands hove into view—Angel and Deer islands. On our right were soon visible a few buildings like those of a farm. These had verdure around them, but not a single tree. This was the presidio.† Around this pseudo-village were seen, for the first time, mules and horses, indicating a settlement.

On the highest hill towered the telegraph, with its long black-&-white arms, arms always in movement to announce the arrival of vessels. Below the telegraph were a few wooden houses and about fifty tents. Opposite the telegraph lay the first anchorage.‡ Here out in the open air was a lazar-house where quarantine inspection was held. Inasmuch as our ship had not touched at any country under suspicion, once having passed quarantine, permission was received to disembark. Several members of our society at once took advantage of this to land and locate a place suitable to erect tents. These tents had to be made of sheets. The promised houses failed

*Probably Fort Point.
†This old Spanish presidio, founded on September 17, 1776, was a low adobe structure called Castillo de Joaquín. The Americans re-named it Fort Montgomery.
‡Yerba Buena anchorage off the foot of Market Street.

to materialize; they were ordered but remained no doubt merely on order, for we never even heard of them again. The members of the company led by Mirandole and Gautier, after going ashore went out to locate what is called French Camp, where French emigrants who had recently come to California usually congregate.

This locality, which was soon discovered, proved ideal. At dawn the following morning, acting on the advice given by our friends, we took pick-axes and shovels, went ashore, and prepared immediately to locate. It was on January eighth, at eight o'clock in the morning, that we first alighted in California, having landed in a sloop belonging to one of our fellow-countrymen who had placed it at the disposal of our company. We deposited our effects at the base of French Camp. In my purse I had one sou, and one centime; and I was in debt ten francs to one of my comrades. This was my entire fortune— but I had finally reached California. A word now about this land which had in store for us so many disillusionizing experiences.

There are two Californias, the old and the new California. The old, which still belongs to Mexico, is bathed on the east by the Vermillion Sea, which derives its name from the exquisite shades of its waters at sunrise and sunset, and on the west and south by the Pacific Ocean. On the north, by an isthmus some twenty-two leagues broad, it joins New California. Cortés was its discoverer. Not far from the Mexican capital which, on August 13, 1521, the Spaniards had recently conquered, the adventuresome captain, who had had two caravels constructed, took command of the expedition &, on May 1, 1535, reached the west coast of the great peninsula.

On the third, he anchored in the bay of La Paz, in 24° 10′ n. lat. and 112° 20′ w. long., taking possession in the name of Charles V, King of Spain and Emperor of Germany.

What is the derivation of the name California, that has endured since the day of its discovery? Does it come from the work of Bernal Diaz of Castille, companion-at-arms and historian of Hernando Cortés?* Does it come, as some say, from *Calida Fornax;* or, as Father Venegas believes, from some Indian word with which the first conquerors might have been unfamiliar or might have neglected to transmit the meaning.†

The ancient capital of this land was Loreto, a town that does not number at the present more than 300 inhabitants. The capital is now San Antonio Real, which has a population of approximately 800.‡ The entire population of this peninsula, which is about 200 leagues long, does not exceed 6,000 souls. New California, called by the English & the Americans Upper California, is situated between 32° and 42° n. lat. and 110° and 127° w. long. From north to south the distance is 250 leagues, and from east to west 300 leagues.§

New California, like the old, was discovered by Spaniards, or rather by a Portuguese, in the service of Spain. This Portuguese was Juan Rodríguez Cabrillo, who departed on January 27, 1542, to attempt definitely to locate the famous passage that, forty-one years earlier, Gaspar de Corteseal believed

Historía Verdadera de la Conquista de la Nueva España, published in 1632.

†The Latin term, *Calida Fornax,* means fiery furnace. In *Las Sergas de Esplandian* by a Spanish writer, Montalvo, published in 1510, occurs the word California. This is the origin usually accepted.

‡San Antonio Real was nothing more than a mining camp; the capital was La Paz.

§The old Spanish league was 2.63 miles. California is 780 miles long and 150 to 350 miles wide.

he had discovered through North America.* This passage, known today as Hudson's Strait, empties into the bay bearing the same name, which resembles an extensive inland sea.

On March 10, 1543, Juan Rodríguez Cabrillo discovered the large Cape Mendocino, naming it Mendoza in honor of the Mexican viceroy of the same name.† On the return voyage he sighted, on November fifteenth, near the thirty-seventh parallel, a vast bay which he named Bahía de los Pinos, or the Bay of Pines. This bay was probably that of Monterey. In 1579, the English navigator, Francis Drake, after destroying a number of Spanish settlements along the South Seas, explored the Californian coast between San Francisco Bay and Point Bodega. Drake, in turn, took possession of the country in the name of Queen Elizabeth of England, naming it New Albion.

Twenty years later, Philip III, casting covetous eyes on this fine land of which he had heard marvelous reports, issued orders to the Conde de Monterey, viceroy of Mexico, to colonize this new country. For this expedition, the viceroy selected one of his bravest and most seasoned mariners. This mariner was called Sebastian Vizcaíno. Leaving Acapúlco on March 5, 1602, Vizcaíno sailed up the coast, exploring as far as Cape Mendocino.‡ Sailing back as far as the Point of Pines, he entered the famous bay which Cabrillo had located, giving to the point where he landed the name of Monterey in honor of the viceroy, as Cabrillo had done at Cape Mendoza.

*Cabrillo sailed North from Natividad on June 27, 1542 to search for the so-called Straits of Anian.
†Cabrillo's ships passed Cape Mendocino in November, 1542. Probably not so-named until later.
‡Vizcaíno's departure was on May 5, 1602.

Hypolite Ferry, in his scholarly work on California, cites the following passage which he extracts from the records of the expedition of Sebastian Vizcaíno.* Even now it is possible to recognize the accuracy of this account made some 250 years ago.

'The climate of this country is mild,' observes the admiral of Philip III, 'the soil, covered with vegetation, is extremely fertile; the country is well-populated; the natives are so human & so docile that it would be simple to convert them to the Christian faith & make them subjects of the Spanish crown.'

The aforesaid Sebastian Vizcaíno, having questioned the Indians and many others whom he found along the shores over a long stretch of the coast, ascertained from them that on beyond their country were several extensive villages and quantities of gold and silver, reports that made him believe great riches might be discovered in these regions. Despite this report, Spain was never cognizant of the immense value of her colony, and was satisfied merely to send governors and missionaries who were protected by military establishments which, even now, are termed presidios.

Gradually the Indians became detached, one by one, from the parent stem; some were conquered by the English or Dutch; others formed empires or independent kingdoms. This same thing occurred with the Republic of Mexico; to this power were united the two Californias.

But before long the inefficient administration of the Mexican republic began to estrange her provinces. Texas, who had declared her independence in 1836, proposed to Congress, on April 12, 1844, a treaty of annexation to the United States.

*Ferry left a volume entitled *Description de la Nouvelle Californie*, Paris, 1850.

This treaty, at first refused by the United States, on December 22, 1845, was definitely adopted by the two houses.* The loss of this territory created a serious problem for Mexico. The Mexican government then decided to raise an army and go to war with the United States over the ownership of Texas. An army of 4,000 men, commanded by Generals Scott and Taylor, was dispatched to defend their rights in Texas. The Mexicans assembled an army of 8,000 soldiers.

On May 7, 1846, the two armies met on the plains of Palo Alto.† A fight ensued; the Mexicans, defeated, retreated across the Rio Grande, & over to the city of Matamoros. Then, on May eighteenth, Matamoros capitulated. At this time the Americans had sent out Commodore John Sloat with a fleet to wage war along the coast, while General Taylor was campaigning in the interior. On July 6, 1846, the American fleet captured Monterey, the capital of New California.‡

By the close of the year, the American land forces had occupied the provinces of New Mexico, Tamaulipas, Nuevo Leon, and Coahuila; while the sea forces had captured California. While marching toward Mexico, General Taylor proclaimed the immense provinces through which he passed to be conquered by the American government, announcing that they had joined the united provinces.

On February 22, 1847, the two opposing forces again clashed in Nuevo Leon, between the southern extremity of the Verde Mountains, and the sources of the Leon, on the plain of Buena Vista. The Americans had a force of 3,400 infantry

*Texas was admitted into the Union under a joint resolution of Congress adopted on March 1, 1845.
†The battle of Palo Alto was fought on May eighth.
‡On July seventh Monterey capitulated.

and 1,000 cavalry. After two days of obstinate fighting, the Mexican army was forced to withdraw to San Luis de Potosí, leaving 2,000 dead on the field of battle. The number of wounded was considerable; but since many had been removed the actual number was not known. The Americans had lost 700 men. 'Another victory like that,' as Pyrrhus remarked, 'and we are lost.'

In somewhat similar vein General Taylor wrote to Congress. Congress at Washington voted nine regiments of volunteers & to every volunteer who served a year in the Mexican war, promised to grant a tract of 160 acres of land or a pension of 100 dollars bearing 6 per cent interest. By the same law the pay of the men in the regular army who were receiving forty-five francs a month was raised. To defray the expense of this war, additional paper to the amount of $28,000,000 was also issued. The American squadron was to seize Vera Cruz, as it had seized Monterey, Vera Cruz being the key to Mexico.

On March 22, 1849, an army of 12,000 men reinforced by Commodore Perry's squadron, laid siege to Vera Cruz & the bombardment commenced. After a siege of five days, the city capitulated, and with it the chateau of San Juan de Ulloa.* On April 16, General Scott left his position and with 10,000 men marched on to Mexico City.

The Mexican army, a force of 10,000 men under General Santa Anna, awaited him two days beyond Vera Cruz in the pass of Cerro Gordo, a veritable Thermopylæ where the Mexican army was destined to meet its fate. The route was broken by a gorge from behind which a formidable artillery stood ready to belch forth fire. From base to summit the

*The siege of Vera Cruz lasted from March 7 to March 29, 1847.

mountain was like an immense entrenchment. The Americans did not hesitate; they attacked the bull, as their enemies the Mexicans say, by the horns. The fighting was terrific. Men fought body to body; horses, cavalrymen and infantry rolling down precipices were killed by the struggle if not killed by wounds. The slaughter lasted four hours. At the end of this period the pass was forced, while the Mexicans left in the hands of their enemy 6,000 prisoners and 30 cannon. On the twentieth, Jalapa capitulated. Eight days later the sturdy fortress of Perotte was finally captured.

General Scott now marched on Puebla, which he occupied. He was now only about twenty-eight leagues from Mexico City. Then, with only 6,000 men he captured the city with its 60,000 inhabitants. On August nineteenth and twentieth he seized the strongholds of Contreras & Churubusco. On September thirteenth General Scott attacked the positions of Chapultepec and Molino del Rey. Finally, on September 16, 1847, the Americans, victorious in all their encounters, entered the capital of Mexico.* On February 2, 1848, after three months of negotiations, peace was signed between Mexico & the United States, by which New Mexico and New California were to be ceded for $15,000,000 to the United States.† The United States was further obligated to satisfy the claims to the amount of $5,000,000 held against Mexico by Texan or American subjects.‡ The total amount over and above the cost of the war, assumed by the Americans, was some 106,-000,000 francs.

*On September thirteenth Mexico City was captured & the war terminated.
†The treaty of Guadalupe Hidalgo; Texas was also included.
‡These claims totalled $3,250,000.

The exchange of ratifications took place on May 3, 1848. On the fourteenth of the following August, the American Congress voted to extend to the people of California the benefits of the laws of the Union. They were just in time; England was already bargaining with Mexico for California, and Mexico probably would never have ceded this if, at this moment as we shall see, the Americans themselves had not been occupying this country.

While Generals Scott and Taylor were seizing Mexico, here is what was occurring in California. In 1845, the white population of California, numbering approximately 10,000, had revolted against Mexico and placed at its head a Californian, named Pico.* To this movement had rallied three leaders of the former government—Vallejo, Castro, and Alvarado.†

General Micheltorena, governor of the country representing Mexico, marched against the insurgents.† On February 20, 1845, he met Castro. The outcome of this fight was that General Micheltorena was defeated. Pico was then made governor of California, while José Castro was placed in command of the army. Micheltorena, aware that he was powerless against such a movement, embarked on an American ship with the officers and soldiers who wished to follow him, and was taken down to San Blas. At this same time an order was sent from Congress, directing Commodore John Sloat to seize Monterey.

The insurgents, subsequently regarding this country as

*Pio Pico subsequently became the last Mexican Governor of California.
†Mariano Vallejo of Sonoma, José Castro, & ex-governor Juan B. Alvarado.
‡Manuel Micheltorena was brigadier-general of the Mexican army and governor of California from 1842 to 1845.

their own & having expelled the Mexicans, now determined to defend it against the Americans.

At this time, on the banks of the Rio Grande at the foot of Mt. Anáhuac in New Mexico, was an American officer in command of a regiment of dragoons, named Stephen W. Kearny. With eyes turned toward California, he was beginning to be perturbed about serious complications to which American residents living out in this country might be exposed, when he received an order from Congress to cross the mountains, travel down along the banks of the Colorado River, & proceed with his regiment across the unknown deserts of the Ajoutas Indians by way of Lake Nicolet to aid the operations of the American squadron & protect the United States citizens located in that territory.*

This was one of those orders issued by governments in their ignorance of localities, that are impossible of execution by those receiving them. In fact, it was impossible to handle an entire regiment in so isolated a region, a land which was the haunt merely of trappers and Indians. Colonel Kearny, taking 100 men, started off with them for California, leaving the balance of his regiment on the banks of the Rio Grande del Norte.

In another section of the country off towards Lake Pyramid, north of New Helvetia, another American officer, Captain Frémont, of the corps of topographical engineers, was exploring California.† Finding himself in the midst of the insurrection, after organizing and assembling a small army

*Probably the land of the Apache Indians.
†This was John C. Frémont, in command of a party of trappers and frontiersmen, ostensibly on an exploring expedition.

of Americans, he outwardly protested the hostile exhibition of the new governor, Pico. Thus from three angles America had already penetrated, or was about to penetrate California. With Commodore John Sloat, Monterey was approached; with Captain Frémont, the United States was entrenched in the plains of the Three Buttes; with Colonel Kearny and his hundred men, her troops passed across the Rocky Mountains.

During the general insurrection there broke out at the same time a minor insurrection. These new insurgents assumed the cognomen of bears. Their standard was known as the Bear Flag—the symbol of the bear. These bears marched on Sonoma, a small village situated at the northern extremity of the bay of San Francisco, and seized the fort.

Castro, one of the leaders of the first uprising, marched to Sonoma ignorant of the fact that on his flank Captain Frémont, having left his position at the Buttes, was moving in the same direction. The two advance-guards—Californian and Mexican—met just below the fort. The American advance-guard had a force of some ninety men; the Californian advance-guard numbered approximately seventy men. Captain Frémont attacked the enemy's advance-guard, scattered it, and mached on the fort, seizing it with all its equipment. The Americans had now reached San Francisco Bay. From this point they took possession of the village, populated almost entirely by Americans.

During the month of October, 1846, Captain Frémont, learning that Commodore Stockton had anchored off San Francisco, went over with 180 volunteers to join him, leaving a garrison at the Fort at Sonoma. Commodore Stockton ordered his scanty forces to embark and proceed to Monterey, which they reached the following day. There they recruited 220 volunteers, forming a total of approximately 400 men.

In the meantime, the American consul, Mr. O. Larkin, returning from Monterey to San Francisco, was taken prisoner by one of the bands of Californians who patrolled the country.* Captain Frémont, upon learning of this, started off in pursuit of this band, overtook it and, scattering it after a brisk short fusillade, rescued Mr. Larkin.

In the meanwhile, after enduring unbelievable fatigue and suffering time and again for the lack of prime essentials, Colonel Kearny, with his 100 men, marched over the Rocky Mountains, crossed the sandy plains of the Navajo Indians, passed the Colorado, &, after traveling through the lands of the Mohave & Yuma Indians finally reached Agua Caliente.

Upon arriving he fell in with a small troop of Americans, commanded by Captain Gillespie, who told him definitely what was taking place in California and warned him that ahead of him was a troop of seven or eight hundred men commanded by General Andrés Pico, who was in control of the country. Colonel Kearny counted his men. There were only 180 all told, but they were resolute and well-disciplined soldiers. He then gave the order to march on the enemy. Americans and Californians clashed on December sixth out on the plain of San Pasqual.

The engagement was terrific; for a time the small American forces were defeated and nearly routed. Ultimately, however, they were victorious. Colonel Kearny, who from then on was made general, received two wounds, and had two captains, one lieutenant, two sergeants, two corporals, and ten

*Thomas O. Larkin, special United States agent residing at Monterey.

dragoons killed. The Californians, on the other hand, lost two or three hundred soldiers.*

The following day, a detachment of marines sent by Commodore Stockton joined Kearny whom they had been sent out to meet. Thus reinforced they continued to march on toward the north. On December eighth and ninth, he had two more clashes with the Californians but in these engagements, as in the first battle, he emerged victorious. At the same time Castro, now a fugitive, encountered Captain Frémont, and after being surrounded by him, capitulated. A few Californian troops still remained in the vicinity of Los Angeles.

Early in 1847, Captain Frémont joined forces with General Kearny. Their combined forces then marched on to Los Angeles where the insurgents, on January ninth and tenth, clashed; on the thirteenth, Frémont & Kearny entered Los Angeles. California was now conquered.† Captain Frémont received the rank of Colonel, being named military governor of the country. During February General Kearny published a proclamation in which he declared that, having been liberated from their allegiance to Mexico, the Californians were now United States citizens.

*This is exaggerated. The losses of the Californians were probably slight.
†The capitulation of Cahuenga, ending the war, was signed January 13, 1847.

V: CAPTAIN SUTTER

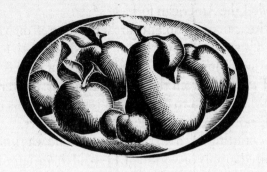

AT THE time the treaty was signed between the United States & Mexico, whereby, for the sum of $15,000,000, Mexico ceded to the United States, New Mexico and New California, there was living in California a man of Swiss descent, John Augustus Sutter, who had been a captain in the royal guards during the revolution of 1830 & who, after the revolution was over, had decided to go out & seek his fortune in America.* After a sojourn of several years in Missouri, in 1836 he left there for Oregon, a country whose resources were just beginning to be noised abroad and into which, since 1832, a few emigrants had been gradually penetrating. Mr. Sutter crossed the Rocky Mountains, traveled over the plains inhabited by the Nez-Percés, the Snake, and the Coeur-d'Alêne Indians, and arrived at Fort Vancouver. From there he sailed over to the Sandwich Islands, finally settling in 1839 in California. Inasmuch as the

*John Augustus Sutter was an internationally known figure and one of the most famous men in California.

governor of the province was at that time encouraging colo-
nization, he gave Captain Sutter a land-grant of some eleven
square leagues, lying on both banks of the Sacramento, at a
point called the American fork.

The Mexican government further conferred on Mr. Sutter
unlimited jurisdiction over his entire district, both for the administration of justice & for the direction of civil & military
affairs. Two miles from the Sacramento Mr. Sutter selected
a little hill on which to establish a residence. This residence
was to be not merely a house; it was to be a fort.

By negotiating with a tribal chieftain he was guaranteed
an unlimited supply of workmen. He paid them definite wages,
that is, he agreed to supply them with suitable food & to pay
them in materials & hardware. These were the men who dug
the trenches for Fort Sutter, made the bricks and erected the
walls. After the fort was built, Sutter recognized the need for
a garrison. This garrison was recruited among the natives.
Fifty Indians were given uniforms, disciplined and instructed
in military tactics. They guarded the fort with the same fi-
delity & certainly more alertly than European troops could
have done.

This fort was made the pretext for a small city called from
the name of its founder, Sutterville. In 1848 this city, or
rather the nucleus of this city, consisted of a dozen houses.
Sutterville lies approximately two miles from the fort. Mr.
Sutter brought into California nearly all our European fruit-
trees, and devoted several hectares of land to their cultivation.* Vines grew especially well and yielded extra fine

*The seeds of fruits and vegetables were brought into California mainly
by the mission Fathers, and by La Perouse, an early French traveler. The
hectare is 2.47 acres.

fruit. But the basic wealth of Mr. Sutter in the days prior to the gold discovery came from raising grain and livestock. In 1848, Mr. Sutter harvested 40,000 bushels of wheat. But in store for him was another extensive source of wealth.

Now the mines of Potosí were discovered by an Indian who went up into the mountains in pursuit of some cattle who had escaped from the main herd. The discovery of the mines along the Sacramento was also the result of a coincidence. Mr. Sutter was in need of planks for construction work; approximately 1,000 feet above the Sacramento Valley grew a remarkably vigorous kind of pine that Mr. Sutter believed would be suitable to supply him with what planks he needed. By a mechanic named Marshall, he arranged to have constructed to handle the pines, a saw-mill turned by a water-wheel.* The saw-mill was constructed according to the agreement, and at the designated locality, but when the water was released & passed over the wheel, the sluice-chamber of this wheel proved to be too narrow to allow water taken in to escape. Inasmuch as a considerable outlay both in time and money would be required to correct this fault, the mechanic merely allowed the amount of water passing through this passage to adjust itself by deepening the sluice-chamber of the wheel. The result was that after several days a mass of sand and detritus formed below the fall.

Upon visiting the saw-mill to find out whether the waterfall had operated in accordance with his expectations, Mr. Marshall discovered in the accumulated sands some brilliant particles which he collected and whose value he soon recognized.† These brilliant bits were pure gold. Mr. Marshall dis-

*James W. Marshall, a workman at Sutter's Fort.
†Gold was discovered at Coloma on January 24, 1848.

closed his discovery to Captain Sutter, both promising to guard the secret. But this was King Midas's secret and in the rustling reeds, in the whispering trees, in the murmuring brooks, were repeated the words that were so soon to be echoed from afar, 'Gold, gold, gold!'

In the beginning this was only a vague rumor, only an intermittent sound, but this was adequate to lure the more adventure-loving inhabitants of San Francisco and Monterey. Soon the official reports of Colonel Mason, of the alcalde of Monterey, of Captain Folsom, and of the French consul, Mr. Moerenhaut were published.* From then on all doubt vanished. The Pactolus was no longer a fable; El Dorado was no longer a myth; the land of gold had been discovered. And from every point of the compass, as if drawn toward the magnetic mountains of The Thousand and One Nights, began to move, as toward a single center, ships from all over the world.

Here is the ratio at which the population was on the increase in California. In 1802, the savant Humboldt, upon compiling statistics, found 1,300 white colonists & 15,562 Indian converts in California. In 1842, Duflot de Mofras made a second tabulation; & from 1,300, the colonists had increased to 5,000.† At the same time, the number of Indians scattered throughout the interior was estimated at 40,000. Early in 1848, the white population totalled 14,000; the native popu-

*The reports of Colonel Richard B. Mason of the United States Army; of Walter Colton, alcalde of Monterey; of Captain Joseph L. Folsom; and Mr. Moerenhaut, of Monterey were circulated throughout the United States and Europe. See Chapter XX, notes 1, 2, 3, and 4.

†Duflot de Mofras was sent out by the French government to investigate conditions on the Pacific Coast. His *Exploration*, published in 1844, is one of the most detailed and accurate accounts of this period. Dumas may have been familiar with his record.

lation however, remained stationary. On January 1, 1849, the white population was 26,000; on April 11, 33,000; on December 1, 58,000. Inside of a few months, these 58,000 were increased by 3,000 Mexicans who had come overland from the province of Sonora; by 2,500 travelers from foreign countries, who arrived by the Santa Fé trail; and by 30,000 emigrants pushing west by way of the northern route. Finally, at the time of our arrival early in January, 1850, the white population amounted approximately to 120,000. By 1855, this will have climbed to a million, and the city of San Francisco will undoubtedly be one of the most densely populated cities of our globe.

This is the law of compensation: The Orient is depopulated for the benefit of the Occident; the birth of San Francisco compensates for the death of Constantinople.

VI : I BECOME A PORTER

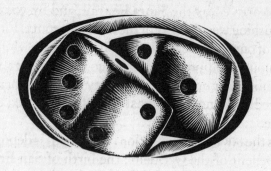

WE ARRIVED in port, as I have said, on the eighth at eight o'clock in the morning. Our first day we passed building embankments, and erecting tents. Four of us went out to look for stakes, some moved dirt, while others constructed tents. I was among the latter.

Of the women, thirteen out of fifteen left immediately for San Francisco where, no matter how impatient they might be to arrive, they were even more impatiently awaited. In fact there were at that very moment in San Francisco, I believe, only about 20 women to 80,000 or 100,000 men. So several ships had left to bring some up from Chile. I have always regretted not having watched to see what happened when our thirteen passengers arrived in San Francisco. Five or six of them did not even go so far as an hotel.

Toward noon the day of my arrival I found my old friend Tillier; he had arrived fifteen days ahead of me & was living at French Camp. Naturally we renewed our friendship with the utmost pleasure, and I shared his cabin until such a time as mine was finished. He was a porter down at the docks.

One of our members had his wife with him; and as she was in charge of the culinary department she sent one of us out after supplies, giving advice about current prices. Our messenger brought back beef to make soup. To have soup was our one ambition; for this was what we had especially missed throughout our voyage. Beef, fortunately, had dropped one-half in price; from five francs it had gone down to fifty centimes a pound. Of our supplies, some sugar and coffee still remained. What our messengers reported was that current prices of all commodities had soared. Bread varied from twenty-five to thirty centimes a pound; however, so we were told, this had recently been worth one piaster.*A room measuring six by eight feet, rented for 500 francs a month, rent to be paid in advance. A small house of three or four rooms rented for 3,000 francs a month.

On Portsmouth Square The El Dorado house had cost 5,500,000 francs to build. This house took in rentals 625,000 francs each month. This is readily understood by explaining that a bricklayer receives from 40 to 60, and a carpenter from 80 to 100 francs daily. Land that was being granted almost gratuitously by the government only six or eight months before our arrival was valued, at the beginning of 1850, at from 100,000 to 150,000 francs for a piece 100 feet square. We saw

*Both the Spanish piaster and the American dollar were legal tender in San Francisco.

one of our fellow-countrymen once purchase at public auction land measuring 45 by 50 feet for 60,000 francs, payable over five years; this he rented for 18 months at a price of 65,000 francs, with the understanding that all improvements made would revert to him at the end of that period.

This same ratio held true with all things, both large and small. Much joking went the rounds about the poor egg-merchant who, watching a seller of marrons make a fortune crying, 'Marrons from Lyon,' was induced to cry, 'Fresh eggs from Lyon.' This merchant may have made his fortune at San Francisco, where eggs just over from France sold for five francs. A story was told about two Gruyère cheeses, that has become almost proverbial in San Francisco; since these were the only Gruyère cheeses that had ever reached port, they belonged to the aristocracy and sold for as much as thirteen francs a pound.

Two boatmen with their skiff received 200 francs for six hours. A pair of sea-boots that reached up above the knees, indispensable articles for walking during the rainy season in the low sections of the city, were worth in winter from 200 to 250 francs, and 100 to 150 francs in the summer season. Physicians were numerous; the majority, however, were charlatans who had been forced to take up other professions. Only three or four had a good reputation and a good following; for professional calls they charged from 45 to 100 francs a visit.

Instances may be cited where almost unbelievable fortunes have been made. Several of our own countrymen who arrived shortly before us with from 100 to 2000 francs in their pockets had, by the time of our arrival, an income of 25,000 francs, not annually, but monthly. All this was in addition to what profits were made in their businesses. As a general thing, such enormous fortunes were derived by renting out buildings, or from land speculations. I nearly forgot to say that later on I went out to buy a small, cheap stove. The price asked was 800 francs. But I was not as yet economical enough to practice such economies. Such tales which strongly suggest fabrications were told to instill both hope and fear in the hearts of poor emigrants who had just landed.

Of the members of our association twenty-five now remained, four having left the first day for the mines. These were the men who had funds. That reports at Valparaiso had been so conflicting was not at all surprising. Even at San Francisco it was difficult to decide on what to rely. The nearest placers, that is, those of the San Joaquín River, were a ten or twelve days' trip from the city. Despite the conflicting rumors that were noised abroad, nevertheless how to go about searching for gold was still the main topic of conversation. Moreover, as we were about to depart for the mines we were harassed by all that would be needed and realized how large an expenditure, even with the utmost economy, was required to be able to ascend the Sacramento or the San Joaquin and become a miner. This is why I say that only the richest men dared start off for the placers.

Now I was not classed among the men of wealth; I have already revealed to the world at large my financial condition. The problem, then, was how to earn what funds were needed for the journey. Luckily in Tillier who had arrived, as I have said, fifteen days in advance, I had an excellent friend to initiate me into local conditions in California. We remained for four days at French Camp, occupied mainly in arranging our tents. Finally, on the fifth day each of us began to work at whatever was at hand, laboring for the common benefit. This community labor, however, lasted only four more days. On the fifth, the organization broke up.

Our first task had been to chop wood in the forests lying on the road to the mission, and sell it. We found a merchant who would purchase this for 90 piasters the cord, approximately 700 francs. The wood was of young oak that burned readily. This wood was carried in on hand-barrows, after being cut and sawed. Anyone was permitted to cut wood. This forest, with the exception of a few little trees that seem to linger on to indicate what these forests once were, is no longer in existence. These same groves now comprise the gardens of the few houses that are just beginning to spring up along the road leading to the mission; one of these days they will be out in the suburbs of the city.

Our organization, as already observed, had lasted just four days; by the end of this period we had earned 100 francs apiece—enough to enable us to live. After this first group had disbanded, every man separated his tent and his belongings from the belongings and tents of his comrades, and started off to make a fortune as best he could. I decided to follow in Tillier's footsteps and his advice was to become a porter like himself. So, being young and vigorous, I went out with my hand-cart and braces to station myself by the corner of a building at the port. This proved, moreover, an excellent occupation for, thanks to the stream of new arrivals, business was flourishing. Tillier and I carried small loads by means of our straps and large loads on our hand-carts. On certain days whereas at such a task I might have earned perhaps five or six francs in Paris, I earned in San Francisco eighteen or twenty piasters.

The Californian has coined the proverb, 'There is no menial task.' I have seen doctors sweeping the streets, and lawyers washing down the decks of vessels. No one is ashamed of this, but shakes hands when meeting friends, and laughs. Every-one leaving for San Francisco should provide a fund of phil-osophy akin to that of Lazarillo de Tormes and of Gil Blas.*
As a matter of fact, out here I became as parsimonious as I had originally been prodigal back in France.

I was now living on five or six piasters daily—thirty or thirty-five francs, a niggardly allowance. But I had a goal to attain. This goal was to save enough for our departure. In-variably I had been confident that the true El Dorado lay at the placers. Within two months I had put away nearly 400 piasters—slightly more than 2,000 francs. Tillier, who had arrived fifteen days before me, had accumulated about 200 piasters more. During the two months I was a porter I had had ample time to go about and inspect the city.

How the city of San Francisco sprang up has already been told. Let us now describe it as it was when we reached there; in other words, less than eighteen months after its foundation. At the time of our arrival California had a population, both at San Francisco & at the mines, estimated at 120,000 men. Our party, as has been said, increased by fifteen the feminine population.

Already in this new world as in the old, where superfluity seems always to form the advance guard of necessity, several

*Lazarillo de Tormes, a Spanish prose epic, by Mendoza, was published in 1554. The French writer, Le Sage, in his Gil Blas drew heavily on the Spanish epic.

theatres had been constructed. Of these, one, which has been mentioned, was up on Washington Street, & here Hennecart had an engagement. To produce comedy in that hall, there was lacking at the time our ship came in, only one thing—actors. Fortunately the same ship that was carrying Mr. Jacques Arago, who remained at Valparaiso as the result of a little disturbance, also brought an actor named Delamarre. Mr. Delamarre started out by engaging two women; one of them arrived on board the *Suffren;* the other came on the *Cachalot.* The *Cachalot*, as will be recalled, was our vessel. The first of these women was known as Hortense; the second, Juliette. Having formed this first nucleus, he recruited actors wherever possible and, one month after our arrival, his troupe was fairly well organized. Until that time the theatre had been used only for masked balls, patterned after those held at *L'Opera;* with the one difference that, because of the shortage of women, flirtations had to be conducted between men.

However, there was one institution that, despite the efforts of theatre-owners to open their doors to the public and their windows to outside breezes, took precedence over concerts, masked balls and performances. These were the gambling houses. No sooner had gold been discovered than a way had to be devised to get rid of it. Gambling provided the means *par excellence.* The interior arrangement of one of these houses was indeed curious. The most fashionable, most frequented, and the richest in gold-dust was the house called El Dorado.

The term gold-dust has been used deliberately, for only on rare occasions were the stakes gold or silver currency. In such houses men actually played with mountains of gold. At both ends of the table stood scales for weighing gold-dust.

When nuggets were exhausted, watches, chains, and jewels were staked. Anything was accepted by the gamblers; anything appraised; anything priced. But the gambler always entered prepared to fight, with a gun on his shoulders and pistols at his belt.

The entire feminine population of San Francisco came to these houses to risk, during the evening, their earnings of the day; they were noted for their zealous gambling and the indifference with which they accepted losses. Absolute equality reigned; bankers and porters rubbed shoulders at the same tables. Here, too, were the bars—long counters over which liquor was sold. All small glasses, all demi-tasses, all cherry or prime brandy sold for two reales Chilian currency—that is, one franc and twenty-five centimes. Musicians were stationed in the room and gave concerts from the morning hours until ten o'clock at night. At ten o'clock, their day being over, they departed. The tired players then rested, while a select few cut one another's throats. The women, as has been said, distinguished themselves by their incessant gambling & their philosophic manner of accepting losses. At this time the feminine population was daily & rapidly on the increase.

That ships were constantly leaving to bring in more women has already been mentioned. Here was a slave-trade of a new sort; one for which no legal provision had been made in the case of ships entering port. Vessels would cast anchor at the most thickly populated places along the coast of South America from Cape Blanc to Valdivia, where appeals were sent out to pretty women whose love of an adventure lured them to try their fortune in California. Moreover in these countries pretty, attractive women speaking Spanish were not uncommon. The captain of the ship would then drive a bargain to transport them for sixty piasters, food & passage included.

Upon arriving in San Francisco, each one sold herself at the best price to the highest bidder among the audience that, attracted by the cargo, congregated. As a general rule the price varied from 300 to 400 piasters; of this amount 60 piasters was returned to the captain. This still left a handsome profit to the woman who, having been the object of speculation, ended by sharing in its profits. Frequently the day after a woman had sold herself for 300 or 400 piasters she felt dissatisfied with her bargain, ran off from her acquirer and sold herself to a new purchaser. Then, inasmuch as there was no law protecting or upholding this traffic, the original purchasers merely lost their 300 or 400 piasters.

Moreover, all other industries were on much the same level. At the head of essential industries should be placed the bakeries. Nearly all the bakers were Americans or Frenchmen who made excellent bread. This bread, which at one time was worth one dollar or one piaster a pound, had, as previously indicated, fallen to one franc, twenty-five centimes. This was the price at the time of our arrival in California; and the price, I presume, at which it is now selling.

Next in importance were the grocers, who were invariably Americans; an unfortunate situation for newcomers who did not understand English. An American grocer who does not understand what you ask for has this in common with a Turkish merchant, namely, that he makes no effort to understand. So if he does not immediately understand what is wanted the customer has to look into the casks, cases, and drawers, and find what is needed. After the customer has found it and placed it on the counter, the grocer then consents to sell what is required.

Then came the *cafés chantants;* these were the large cafés that attracted many customers; the most important at this time were three known as the Café de Paris, the Café des Aveugles, and the Café du Sauvage. Many of the same little songs were sung that might be heard at cafés on the Champs-Elysées. In the Café de l'Independence the singing was superior; there grand opera could be heard. Only what was consumed was paid for. Yet the price of this was high. A small glass, as has been said, was worth two Chilian reales; a bottle of milk sold for one piaster; a bottle of Bordeaux for three piasters; and a bottle of champagne for five.

The restaurants were managed for the most part by the Chinese who handled them in Chinese fashion; even their cooking was abominable. The hotel-proprietors were French; this was obvious from the names on their hotels. These were the Hotel da La Fayette; the Hotel Laffitte; the Hotel des Deux-Mondes. A few charming milliners had established shops, but since there were only, at the time of my arrival, about twenty or twenty-five women, & at my departure only about two or three hundred, those who relied solely for support on the profits from their establishments would have starved. However, about the time I left California these establishments were just beginning to prosper.

Gradually the agriculturalists arrived, bringing seeds. They visited various locations, purchased land that suited them & began clearing. These lands belonged to the American government, or to emigrants from Mexico. The purchasers usually paid for their lands out of what they raised. Don Antonio & his brother, Don Castro, owing to their industry are worth today some five or six millions.* They own all the lands east of the bay of San Francisco where vast herds graze on their holdings.

The method of locating gold, the most seductive and the most popular of all occupations, an occupation that had lured Tillier and me, and whose brilliant promises had given us the courage to make such economies, now merits discussion.

*This probably refers to the Rancho San Lorenzo, seven leagues square, owned by Guillermo Castro and Francisco Soto.

VII : THE PLACERS

Now THAT we had acquired the amount we had fixed as our goal, that is, when I had 400 & Tillier 600 piasters, we decided to leave San Francisco & push on to the placers. What remained was to choose between the region of the San Joaquín & the Sacramento. The advantages & disadvantages of both locations were debated, our final decision falling on the San Joaquín as being closer than the Sacramento. Its mines, moreover, were reputed to be equally rich.

This trip proved epochal. For one thing, the local steamers —this traffic, which has not heretofore been mentioned, was one of the most important enterprises in California—made a rate, exclusive of food, of fifteen piasters each for the trip up to Stockton. Moreover, since the most accessible placers, which almost invariably follow the course of the small subsidiary streams of the San Joaquín or the Sacramento, were, as in the case of the San Joaquín, about twenty-five or thirty leagues beyond Stockton, at Stockton a mule had to be purchased to transport to the mines the necessary supplies and equipment. Our working equipment, as well as our tent, was purchased in San Francisco before our departure for, oddly enough, prices soared in proportion to the distance inland.

Our tools included shovels, pick axes, picks, and cradles. One cradle was sufficient for both Tillier and me, since by working together the labor was divided, one man mining while the other washed. The cradle, a device used for washing gravel, is a tray made of wood or tin measuring twelve or sixteen inches in diameter. This is conical in shape but fairly shallow, & entirely smooth inside. These trays, based on their size, hold from eight to twelve liters and are filled two-thirds full of soil which is beaten and thoroughly washed by holding the tray under water, thus separating the gold from the sand and gravel. To bring extra water and to keep the cradle constantly rocking so that it will separate and turn up every little particle of gold, is the task of the miner who must frequently remain in water up to his waist. The other miner makes the hole & removes the gravel from this excavation.

Having left San Francisco, we finally reached Stockton. On our journey we ascended Suisun Bay, passing on our left five or six islands which had not as yet been named, but which some day will have gardens like those on the islands of Asnières and Neuilly. Arriving at the point where the Sacramento & the San Joaquín fork, we left the Sacramento, which bends from there toward the north, & followed the San Joaquín which, swerving abruptly, winds toward the south. The first affluent of the San Joaquín is formed by the junction of three rivers; the Cosumnes, the Mokelumne and a third, or central river, which has not as yet been named.* These streams water plains of extraordinary fertility, which were overgrown with wild weeds, especially mustard, whose flowers of a brilliant yellow had dropped off and lay glistening like the gold for which we were searching, on the dark foliage of the oaks. Here and there were seen hills covered with splendid oats of such height that a man on horseback was almost entirely concealed by them. Twenty miles below the Calaveras empties in turn into the San Joaquín River. The latter moves through splendid prairies of grass yellowed by the sun; its entire course is lined by oaks and by an exquisite shrub with a mass of blue flowers whose fragrance drifted over to us.

At Stockton, a newly created city, as its name indicates, and one which had sprung up within the last two years, we purchased two mules and the necessary provisions. These mules cost 120 piasters each. Our provisions included fifty pounds of flour which, being damaged, was quite cheap, and which, thanks to this damage, could be purchased at the rate of fifty pounds for seven piasters. For twenty-two piasters we purchased two hams; fifteen pounds of biscuits cost fifty centimes a pound. A can of lard cost two and one-half piasters. Twenty pounds of beans and three or four pounds of salt sold for twelve sous a pound.

After these purchases had been completed and the expense of the journey from San Francisco to Stockton paid, of my 400 piasters only 120 were now available. One mule was soon loaded with our utensils, the other with our provisions. Our destination was Camp Sonora, approximately forty leagues

*Subsequently called Dry Creek.

beyond Stockton & beyond Mormon Diggings, between the Stanislaus & the Tuolumne rivers. We expected to find game along these forty leagues. I had my gun, my bayonet, and my brand new pistols; none of my equipment had been used. Tillier, who was also a good hunter, was equally well-armed.

In traveling from Stockton to the Stanislaus, the first river encountered, the route lay across superb plains studded with trees, and carpeted with the blue flowers already mentioned. These I recognized upon inspecting them more closely as lupines. Another flower of a red-orange color that preferred the shade of oaks and which I have since ascertained was the California poppy also flourished. All the groves of trees were inhabited by handsome birds such as blue-jays, with their speckled heads, pheasants, and by the alluring crested part-ridge, a bird indigenous to California. What quadrupeds we met were primarily gray and yellow squirrels, hares with enormous ears, and rabbits as large as rats. We frightened a few deer, but failed to kill them.

Above the Stanislaus, which was crossed on a bridge of boats—for which, I should like to add, the charge was one piaster each—we again caught the trail that led us through more dense woods. We now began to ascend the first low ranges of the mountains. When not swerving off to the right or left to hunt, we had a good trail well-worn by mules and wagons along which we constantly encountered caravans carrying supplies and merchandise to the mines, or returning empty-handed to take on loads at Stockton or San Francisco. At the approach of dusk we erected our tents, wrapped up in our blankets, and went to sleep.

Five days after our departure from Stockton we reached

Sonora. At Sonora we rested, however, only twenty-four hours, for we learned from acquaintances and from comrades who had come out with us and whom we happened to meet out here that the mines were poor. But we were informed at the same time that in the vicinity of Pine Pass new mines had been discovered that were rumored to be far richer.*

Pine Pass lay some three or four leagues from Sonora in a deep valley wedged in between two mountains. Already a road had been opened from Camp Sonora to Pine Pass that ran through vast forests of oak and pines, forests more abundant in game than any we had yet found. Having reached Pine Pass on toward six o'clock in the evening, there was barely time to place our mules out in pasture, put up our tents, and prepare supper before dark. Moreover, we were so impatient to start work that we looked for a place to dig that same evening. Thereupon we found out that in this region claims could not be selected by miners but were allotted to them by an alcalde.†

So we presented ourselves at the alcalde's dwelling; he was living like any ordinary mortal in a tent. Fortunately he was a kind man who received us pleasantly. To occupy his idle moments he kept on hand a supply of liquor; this was the reason why he encouraged as many miners as possible to locate in his neighborhood. Sympathizing moreover with our impatience, he went out at once and staked off our location. Our task was now to assure ourselves the following morning whether or not this claim was good. The selection made, we

*Passo del Pin, according to the French text. This may have been the French interpretation of the Spanish term, Paso del Pino. This has been translated as Pine Pass. Possibly Pine Log.

†An alcalde was a Spanish official who combined the duties of mayor, police officer, and justice of the peace.

then had a little drink with the alcalde before going over to our quarters.

The following day at seven o'clock in the morning we started work, both digging in an area of six square feet for the long-coveted treasure. At a depth of two feet we struck rock. This chance discovery seriously complicated our situation, for we had none of the instruments necessary to break or extract this; so we dug down below and blew up the rock with powder. We could have blown up a cathedral, so engrossed were we in our work. For five days we continued to extract rock from the ground. Finally, on the sixth day a reddish soil indicating the presence of gold was uncovered. This reddish soil usually tops, for a depth of one to one and one-half feet, auriferous gravel; it is fine, light, and soft to the touch, being composed almost entirely of silica.

Having reached the auriferous strata, we filled our cradle, hurried over to the small stream at Pine Pass, & commenced the operation of washing. As a result of our labors we took out some gold-dust. What was secured was worth perhaps ten francs.

Though it was not the first gold we had seen, yet it was equally rich and was the first we had collected ourselves. Mediocre as was our first washing, yet we were far from feeling discouraged. But we worked for eight days & during these eight days did not secure more than thirty piasters of gold.

Then, convinced that the mine would not support the miner, realizing that our supplies were being exhausted, and having learned that over on the slopes of the Sierra Nevada richer diggings were being found, we packed up our tents, loaded our mules, & started off again. This was on May 1, 1850.

VIII : THE SIERRA NEVADA

The SIERRA NEVADA, otherwise known as the snow-capped chain, toward which we were wending our way, extends from northwest to southeast throughout the entire length of California. This chain is far loftier than the Californian range. Eternal snows crown its summits. Lavishly endowed by nature, at almost regular intervals may be seen large wooded plateaus from which rise volcanic peaks that tower from 12,000 to 15,000 feet above sea-level.

These isolated, eternally snow-capped peaks have given to this range the name of Sierra Nevada. This chain rises gradually, step by step, the first hills being followed by mountains, while the mountains become more & more precipitous the nearer they approach the region of eternal snows. The distance from base to summit averages from twenty-six to twenty-eight leagues.

As in the Alps, this space is divided into regions where certain trees thrive to the exclusion of all others; at the base of the mountains are found oaks; above the oaks rise cedars; above the cedars tower pines. However, the pines that thrive in the higher altitude & which usually crown the mountains grow also in the lower ranges.

The region between the Californian range and the Sierra Nevada contains all those rich gold deposits that have lured to California all the varied representatives of the human race who have come from all over the globe. By uniting on the south these mountain ranges form the vast Tulare Valley, if not the most fertile, at least one of the most fertile in California.

On the morning of our departure, which occurred at eleven o'clock, having realized that our tin cradle operated slowly and gave only mediocre results, we decided to build our own cradle to wash gravel. Unfortunately, we lacked nearly everything required for making such a machine. The bottom of the machine consisted, first of all, of a dozen planks six inches in breadth and two or three feet in length. If we made these planks ourselves we should lose time that was becoming more and more valuable; to purchase these planks required more funds than we could supply.

Suddenly the thought came to me to go over to American Camp, situated one and one-half leagues from the diggings where we knew wine was being shipped in kegs. There we purchased two old empty kegs for one piaster each, and some nails at an exorbitant figure. All that was now needed was a piece of sheet iron. I was fortunate enough to find, just after we had decided to make this acquisition, a piece of old iron, attached to a mule saddle which had served, no doubt, for a lining.

At eight o'clock that morning we returned to our tent and began work on our machine which we completed in about two hours, with the aid of a saw, a plane, and our knives. We then went out to try it & see how it worked. Our work proved entirely successful. There was nothing more to hinder us from leaving for the Sierra Nevada & locating some good placers.

At eleven o'clock, as I have said, we departed, climbing the first mountain that loomed up ahead of us. Out here there was no longer a well-traveled trail. With the sun's rays pouring down on us, we moved on through the high grass of which I have already spoken. The mules led us at random; and in all justice to them it must be said that they knew how to find the best route. This did not prevent us, from time to time, in falling down literally from fatigue under groves of trees, groves composed almost invariably of pines and oaks.

Twice during this trip we found running water & descended to the river. At the second stream we stopped, watered our mules, allowed them to graze a bit, and had something to eat ourselves. At five o'clock in the evening we resumed our course. We intended to camp at the top of the mountain, but we did not reach the summit until after nine-thirty at night. The moon shone in full force. We did not meet any troublesome animals, although we had heard many tales about rattlesnakes, vipers, & even boa constrictors. But all of them shun man and if for some reason they appear, it is, as I shall soon explain, merely to seek warmth.

So we camped quietly that night, intending to leave at

dawn the following morning. One thing, however, perturbed us; we knew that the ascent had been difficult, but we did not know what the descent might disclose. At dawn we discovered a gentle slope, all prairies & forests; this slope led up to the banks of the Murphy, one of the principal affluents of the Stanislaus River. There was water everywhere, much like a corner of paradise. But alas, this was far from being a paradise for gold-seekers; even as the wandering Jew ordered behind him the angel who said 'Go,' so the miner had behind him a devil who said to him, 'Search.'

Upon approaching the banks of the river, its shores were found to be quite steep. Along these banks we traveled for nearly an hour, camping about one kilometer from a high mountain that we had skirted, seven or eight hours beyond the first slopes of the Sierra Nevada. By dawn the following morning we were again on our way. Since leaving Sonora we had not met a single person.

Of the many gold-seekers who had already attempted this same journey and had reached their destination, all had arrived at the season when the snows were melting & when the torrents of water that were pouring down from the mountains had submerged the lower plains on which was found gold. We arrived about ten o'clock in the morning at the point toward which we had started. On several plateaus, all more or less elevated, we discovered traces of old diggings. This indicated that up here excavation was necessary. We then erected our tent, pastured our animals, and set off to locate claims. Inasmuch as surface indications were not conclusive, it was all a matter of good luck or misfortune.

We now began to work, but no sooner had we dug down

to a depth of two feet than water gushed up whenever we used axes. This water made work virtually impossible. So we climbed up the slope that lay ahead of us and made two or three more holes but unfailingly, at a greater or lesser depth, we encountered water. However we did not entirely lose hope for we had run through several layers of reddish soil. But upon being washed these produced nothing. Then we decided to make a new channel, a channel being the means used to increase or alter the course of a stream. In this way we took out a few bits of gold, but not in paying quantities. We returned to our tent profoundly discouraged. This time we were aware that our dreams had vanished in the face of stern reality. We had spent over 600 piasters but had taken in less than 200 francs in gold!

We dined, however, with fairly good appetites, for all we now had to rely on was our own strength. Dinner that night included ham soup, a few beans left over from the previous evening, and tortillas in place of bread. The tortilla is a kind of wheat cake flattened between the hands and cooked in ashes. Supper over, preparations were made for the night. At the altitude at which we were camping, that is, approximately 3,000 feet above sea-level, the nights began to be crisp. This condition forced us to keep ignited throughout the night the fire used for cooking supper; this being located near the opening of our tents also served to warm our feet.

We were just dropping off to sleep when off in the distance sounds resembling prolonged and plaintive wails were heard. Both of us, hearing these sounds simultaneously, were soon wide awake & at once reached instinctively for our guns. A few seconds later more cries like the first were heard approaching;

these we now knew meant wolves. The howling pack appeared to be descending the same mountain we had passed that afternoon. The nearer they approached the more their yaps increased. We threw off our covers & cocked our guns. Luckily the alarm proved short-lived; the wolves, following down the banks of the Murphy, disappeared into the mountains.

In all probability they would have injured neither us nor our mules. Our principal anxiety was for our mules for they were picketed out some forty feet away. We went out, gun in hand, to look after them, then moved them over and tied them to the stakes of our tent to await the dawn. The balance of the night passed quietly, enabling us to get some sleep.

At daybreak we started off once more. This time we retraced our steps and, instead of ascending the Murphy, went downstream. On toward eleven-thirty we stopped for food, and at one o'clock began digging again. Here we continued to find some water, but not enough to prevent work. At a depth of from five to six feet reddish soil was uncovered. This proved to be a type of gravel that looked highly favorable. Having assembled and separated it, after five hours labor we collected nearly one ounce of gold, that is, gold valued at 90 or 100 francs.

Having finally found a good location we decided not to move again. Our spirits rose in contrast to the depression of the previous evening and we anticipated still better luck the day following, for we had worked only five hours. The next day we hoped to double our labor. That evening we had taken the precaution of bringing our mules close in and building a roaring fire. However, fearing a shortage of wood, while I prepared supper Tillier took his hatchet and went out to bring in firewood. Ten minutes later I saw him, by the light of the moon, coming back to our tent; he had no fire wood but kept glancing behind, visibly preoccupied with something on which his eyes were fastened in the semi-obscurity of the night.

'Hello,' I called out, 'what's the matter?'

'The trouble is,' he replied, 'that we are among wolves and they have located us this evening.'

'Nonsense!'

'My dear fellow, I've just seen one.'

'A wolf?'

'Yes, he was coming down the mountain; we both saw each other at the same time and both stopped.'

'Where was that?'

'About 100 feet back. Since he did not move, neither did I; but I was afraid this might last a long time & that you might be uneasy so I came back.'

'And the wolf?'

'When he did not see me any longer he must have continued on his way.'

'Suppose we take our guns & look into the situation more closely.'

Taking our guns which, after our experience last evening, were kept constantly loaded, Tillier walked ahead, while I followed close behind him. Some thirty feet back from the river Tillier stopped and, motioning for me to be quiet, pointed with his finger at a wolf sitting by the banks of one of the small streams that flow down and empty into the Murphy.

Of his presence there was no doubt; his two eyes, fixed on us, shone in the night like two glowing coals. Almost simultaneously we took aim with our guns; simultaneously was heard the noise of shots. The wolf fell over, nearly rolling into the river. From the mountains thundered the reverberation of our combined shots. We went up to the wolf. He was dead. The two balls had struck—one in his neck, the other in his chest. We dragged him as far as our tent.

The night now grew hideous; packs of wolves circled constantly around us. Our frightened mules shook and trembled from head to foot. Though our fire kept the wolves at a safe distance, yet we had no sleep that night.

IX: THE AMERICANS

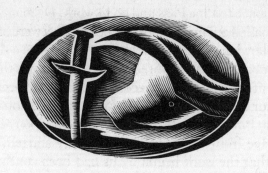

To CONTINUE to remain on where we were was now impossible; the wolves, warded off one night, might return the following night, grow bolder, devour our mules, and perhaps even us. Such was not our object in coming to California. So the following morning we continued to travel down along the river, dig holes, and make channels.

While we collected some gold, yet the amount was small, not over one franc a cradle. Certainly no other place equalled the diggings we had left. We were talking together—feeling braver by daylight—to ascertain if in spite of wolves we dared return, when suddenly we perceived a black bear tranquilly descending the mountain. The temptation to open fire was almost overpowering. But a tradition given strong credence in California restrained us; for the Indians are of the belief that a bear wounded by hunters goes back and enlists other bears and that all unite and return to attack the hunter.

This seemed highly improbable; but not being acclimated as yet to solitude and isolation and being unfamiliar with this new country, we felt somewhat timid. So we concluded to return at once to Pine Pass and go to work. Dismantling our tent, we loaded our mules, took our bearings, & were off again.

The following day in a patch of green pasture a deer was sighted grazing. Both of us fired & both shots struck the mark. This was at the same time an economy & a good speculation. We cut our deer into pieces and, loading this on our mules, sold half at Pine Pass for twenty-five piasters. Upon returning to the place from which we had originally started, we discovered that the work begun by us had been continued by others, then finally abandoned for lack of tools. All the workers found gold; but it was only those who were organized in large groups that accomplished anything. But societies or rather group organization with its concomitant responsibilities are naturally distasteful to Frenchmen; whereas, on the other hand, Americans seem to have a predilection for organization.

Out here I had an example of the rapacity of doctors. An American who was ill sent out for a doctor, an American like himself. This doctor called three times & charged one ounce of gold for each visit. He also sold him a dose of quinine and charged two ounces. This was approximately 425 francs. The result was that in California an invalid preferred to die rather than call in a doctor.

At Pine Pass there were, I should judge, about 120 or 130 workers. Moreover, thirty-three Frenchmen from Bordeaux and Paris had assembled and, a little below the camp, had turned the course of the river. This task had required some four months. During this period they had consumed all their supplies and exhausted their capital.

Just as they were about to reap the fruits of their sacrifice, 120 Americans who had been merely biding their time appeared & declared that they held Pine Pass; that the river was a subsidiary of the American River; that in consequence no one but Americans had the right to turn aside the stream; and that they must leave, for if they refused, since they had 120 strong and well-armed men, not a Frenchmen would be left along the river. Now the French were clearly within their rights, but the alcalde, being an American, naturally sided with his fellow-countrymen.

Pressure was brought to bear on the French to yield. Some withdrew to San Francisco; others went to Sonora; others left for Murphy's Camp; others, finally, remained to make channels hoping to return not entirely empty-handed. In the end the robbery failed materially to benefit the Americans. Rumors of this outrage soon spread throughout the countryside; all the French at Mormon Bar and Jamestown congregated, remained hidden between two mountains and, during the night, turned the river back to its normal channel.

The following morning the Americans found the river at Pine Pass flowing in its former channel. So no one derived any profit after toiling for four months, although these labors might perhaps have brought in a million. Aware that there was no place for us at Pine Pass, we returned to the camp at Sonora where the alcalde had originally allotted us a claim.

The distance, it will be recalled, from Pine Pass to Sonora was three or four leagues. We arrived at eleven o'clock in the evening, pitched our tent where it had been placed before, & occupied ourselves in preparing our usual supper, which had not been in any way changed except when supplemented by game, and which invariably comprised ham and beans.

The following morning we decided to work at a test channel. The formation here consisted of a kind of loam, mixed with clayish schist and slate, which came off in flakes that dissolved in water. There Tillier and I were able to extract approximately eighty francs of gold daily. This barely covered our expenses, for our provisions were now nearly exhausted. We worked, however, in this way for an entire week—from Monday morning until Saturday night.

On Sunday, a day of rest, all work stopped at the mines. So we decided to consecrate this day of rest to a hunting-trip. But even the game, too, now began to grow scarce and to withdraw far into the mountains. Notwithstanding, we killed two or three pheasants and several of those charming crested partridge of which I have already spoken.

That evening we returned, saddened by the fact that the hunting, as well as mining, gave evidence of being a failure. Upon our return we fell in with a poor French cook, who had deserted from a French whaler. He was of the belief that he merely needed to spade up the soil to make a fortune in California. We commenced to revise his ideas immediately. His bedding—his sole possession—was all he carried with him. For a few days he enjoyed the use of our supplies and the fruits of our hunting expedition. Since he spoke Spanish, we believed that he might in some way prove useful.

After testing him for a few days and finding his personality agreeable, we took him in with us. In addition to acting as our interpreter, he rendered us one invaluable service. He taught us how to make bread. Our bread was kneaded in the cradle. Having no yeast we had to manage without it. Spreading a bed of coals on the ground, the bread was placed on top, then covered as in cooking potatoes. When the bread was cooked we scraped off the ashes. This made a very heavy and indigestible bread; but it was an economical bread—for we ate less of it. At the placers, wheat cost from fifty-five sous to three francs the pound.

On Monday morning we decided to try another hole. We moved on to a point called Yaqui, adjoining the placers where we had been working. There we found five or six miners already in ahead of us. Having been lured by some dazzling bits of gold that had been found there, we dug a hole. For the first four feet we found a gray soil, resembling a volcanic product more than the usual type of soil. Aware that such soil carried no gold-dust we concluded not to give it a washing. Below this gray soil appeared a reddish substance and the operation of washing now began.

After taking in approximately eight piasters in gold, Tillier unexpectedly found a nugget that must have weighed four ounces. This made about 345 francs that we had uncovered in one lump. By way of celebrating, we now indulged in a bottle of Saint Julian wine at a cost of five piasters. This was on May twenty-fourth. Our labors were for the first time meeting with success.

But on the morning of May twenty-seventh, just as we were starting off to work, we saw circulars tacked upon the trees. These announced that, starting from the twenty-seventh, no foreigners could dig except upon payment to the American government of a tax of twenty piasters for each man working a claim.*

*The State legislature had placed a prohibitive tax of twenty dollars a month on all foreigners engaged in mining in California. Thousands were now forced to abandon their claims.

This gave us food for thought; the miner now gambled not only his time & labor, but he also had to risk a comparatively large sum of money. Our hole was already quite extensive, and would soon touch neighboring diggings. We would have to pay sixty piasters to keep it, or sixty piasters before digging another hole. About ten o'clock, while debating what course to pursue, we saw a group of armed Americans who had come to collect the tax. We refused to pay. This refusal was the signal for war. We had less than 120 or 130 Frenchmen in all.

However, all the Mexicans at the mines joined forces with us, saying that they too owned the soil as well as the Americans. Since they had about 4000 men all told, these added to the other recruits would have made quite an imposing army. The Americans on the other hand numbered about 2500 or 3000 miners. These men proposed that we organize & resist, forming an army. To us & to other Frenchmen were offered the rank of officers in this army. Unfortunately, or rather fortunately, we knew our men; at the first serious clash they might even desert and turn against us. So we declined.

From this time on our lives were no longer safe at the placers. Day after day reports came in not of one death but of three or four murders committed either by Mexicans or by Americans. The only difference lay in the method used by the murderer. The Americans would come over to the edge of the diggings and, without any discussion, kill a miner with their pistols. Then, should one miner attempt to come to the aid of his comrade, he too would be killed with a shot.

The Mexican, on the contrary—and nearly all the Mexicans were from the province of Sonora—would approach in a friendly manner, chat, ask news of the diggings and, with a blow from his knife, kill the very man with whom he had been chatting.* Two of our fellow-countrymen were killed in this manner, but by Americans. Two Mexicans even made an attempt on us; but we came off victorious, killing both.

Then, aware that the outcome would undoubtedly be a massacre in which we should probably be the losers, we sent messengers to Mormon Bar, Murphy's Camp, Jamestown and Jacksonville to call the French to our assistance. The following day 350 Frenchmen came over with knapsacks on their backs, fully armed.

The Americans on their part had issued an appeal to their countrymen, & received reinforcements of one hundred men who came in from neighboring placers. Toward eight o'clock in the evening the French reinforcements made us fully aware of their protection by pitching camp between two mountains which commanded the trail. We also armed and, abandoning our diggings, went to rejoin these arrivals. A few Americans, more honest than the others, took sides against their fellow-countrymen & came over to our camp. Two hundred Mexicans had followed us; the rest, realizing that a clash was imminent, had vanished.

We now took up positions on the crest of the two mountains that commanded the trail. Our 350 compatriots remained on horseback on the main trail. We had, all told, some 700 men. Our position was favorable; we could indefinitely intercept all communications with Stockton. Several Americans and men from other countries were stopped.

*The name Sonora was given by the Sonoran diggers who originally camped at this point. By 1849 it was the largest and gayest camp in California, having a population of 5,000.

The night was passed standing guard. The following day toward us was seen advancing a detachment of about 150 Americans. We now hid in the tall grass and behind trees, leaving only a lookout visible behind barricades hastily thrown up along the route. The Americans, believing themselves sufficiently numerous to dislodge us, began the attack. Thereupon, our men jumped out of hiding; from both mountains fire now blazed forth simultaneously, & twenty Americans fell dead or wounded. The rest fled in a body, scattering on the plains and seeking shelter in the woods. The fugitives returned to Sonora. But the following morning we saw them reappear, the alcalde marching at their head, carrying a cross aloft. They reported that they had written to the governor & were awaiting his reply. A truce was accordingly arranged.

In the meanwhile, each man was free to return to his diggings. How cautiously each miner came back is self-evident, for his life hung constantly by a mere thread. The expected letter arrived; in this was confirmed the twenty-piaster tax, while the alcalde was given the right of life and death over all foreigners. To live longer at Sonora was now impossible. So we sold all our equipment and purchased enough supplies to carry us back to Stockton. From Stockton we planned to return to San Francisco. But what could we do there? We did not know. At Stockton our mules were sold for 200 piasters. With these funds we purchased supplies & engaged accommodations on a boat leaving for San Francisco.

This time the trip was made far more rapidly, for we were going downstream. The banks of the San Joaquín were covered with reeds; in the reeds lived a motley & numerous throng of sea-wolves & tortoises. These reeds adjoined marshy woods in which, though inhabited by charming birds, deadly fever also lurked. On beyond these reeds and marshy woods stretched magnificent prairies on which roamed vast herds of cattle. Here and there the prairie was burning. Had some accident or some malicious act started this fire, or had it been kindled by the excessive heat? Our pilots were ignorant of its origin. The trip down required three days; but upon reaching the mouth of the river we encountered considerable difficulty in entering the bay itself; the tide was high and there were head winds. We could not at first overcome this double obstacle.

Finally, after surmounting these difficulties, on Thursday morning, June twenty-second, we entered San Francisco harbor where some wharves newly covered with houses were discovered. Wharves & houses had been built in our absence —an absence that had lasted only four months. Utterly exhausted, Tillier and I decided to rest for two or three days, deferring until later the decision as to what should be our future occupation. Our comrade, the cook, had remained at the mines.

X : THE SAN FRANCIS-CO FIRE

WHEN I SAY we hoped to rest two or three days, I may perhaps have exaggerated our intentions, for upon our arrival what we had hoped for—to live at a hotel—was checked by the condition of our finances. What we actually did was to erect our former tent with our old blankets.

French Camp was where we decided as usual to reside. French Camp, as the name indicates, was the general rendez-vous of our fellow-countrymen; however, since our departure among the primitive tents had sprung up like so many mush-rooms, a dozen wooden houses occupied by laundries run both by men and women.

Upon leaving for the mines we had placed our trunks in the house of an old German who, being too old to engage in active work, made a specialty of looking after the belongings of workers. Furthermore, this occupation he had selected was far from proving a poor business. He had erected a kind of shed, where he stored small trunks for two piasters a month and large trunks for four piasters. This brought him in from 1500 to 1800 francs a month. Having erected our tent, we were just putting our trunks away when we suddenly heard the cry 'Fire.'

Fires, by the way, occur constantly in San Francisco for since wood is in general use a constant series of fires is unavoidable. Every inhabitant of California who has debts to pay has a fire! This applies even to gambling debts. The fire heralded by these cries proved to be a first-class fire. It started between Clay and Sacramento streets, the section occupied by merchants dealing in wines and lumber.

By wine merchants I mean merchants selling both wines & liquors. Fanned by a vigorous north breeze the fire spread rapidly, affording from the heights from which we watched it spread a magnificent spectacle. Alcohol and wood-yards, what more could the most fastidious fire require?

At each fresh supply of rum, brandy, or spirituous liquors that the fire touched, its intensity was redoubled; simultaneously the flames changed color. This might have been aptly termed a magnificent illumination of Bengal fires, with its reds, blues, and yellows. This was intensified by the American habit of handling fires by hurling tons of powder on the flames in the belief that the house, by falling, will check this monster. The house in fact collapses, but almost invariably its flaming embers fall over across the street, setting fire to those located on the opposite side which, being built of wood and already hot from the proximity of the flames, catch fire like so many matches.

At the present time, wooden pavements have been laid for greater convenience & consequently when fire starts nothing can stop it; moreover with rare intelligence a fire invariably starts just when the water supply is especially low, and since the city is always short of water even for drinking purposes, the fire moves ahead without fear of being checked in its mad progress.

But owing to this water shortage, for the consolation of those who have fires there is a corps of well-organized firemen who at a given signal rush over with splendid pumps to the scene of the disaster. These pumps are absolutely empty, but they can pump air, and this usually has a tendency to stifle the flames.

While reluctant to say that these fires are caused deliberately, yet right in the city of San Francisco there are so many men who are interested in having San Francisco burn down that a certain amount of suspicion is inevitable. For instance, on that day wine merchants and lumber merchants were wiped out by fire. While this fire may have ruined its immediate victims, yet it enriched dealers in lumber and wines in other sections of the city, not to mention the owners, proprietors, and consignees of vessels that were waiting to unload, and that carried cargoes similar to what had been lost in the conflagration.

On the morning of the fire common wine had risen, for example, from 100 to 600 and 800 francs a puncheon, clearly quite an advance.

Recalling at this time that two of our friends, Gauthier &

Mirandole, were living in a house adjoining the burning section (they lived on Kearney Street and had a bonded warehouse for consignments) we ran to their assistance only to find them dismantling their building. Now to move out under such conditions is almost suicidal, for to transport furniture or goods from the city to the hill, the owners of moving vans ask 100 francs for each trip. How invalids frequently preferred death to sending for a doctor has already been intimated. With a fire close by the majority are almost as willing to be burned out as to call for wagons to carry off their merchandise. Everyone in San Francisco, furthermore, is very obliging, almost too obliging. Everyone comes to your assistance, everyone puts a shoulder to the wheel, and it is amazing how furniture disappears in the hands of its movers.

To give any idea of the noise made under such conditions by the Americans is virtually impossible. They come, go, scamper here and there, shout, enter the houses, break and destroy things, & above all, become intoxicated. In addition to all this, no sooner has a house burned down, than everyone digs with anything at hand among the ashes; not only at the mines is there a frenzy of gold-digging!

Among the block of burning buildings was a steel house that had come out from England, where it had been constructed. Owing to the material of which it had been built the natural expectation was that it would defy the flames. Everyone, in consequence, carried, rolled, pushed, & piled up what he had of most value inside this building. But the fire proved insatiable. Upon reaching the steel edifice, it was soon enveloped with tongues of flame that lapped at it greedily, surrounding it with such intense heat that the steel began to turn red, writhe, & cringe, as did all the adjoining wooden houses. Of the entire house and its contents, all that remained was a kind of formless, shrunken, shriveled hull whose original shape could no longer be recognized.

The fire traveled from north to south, being finally stopped at California Street, a broad thoroughfare which the fire, despite its relentless efforts, was unable to leap. The fire had lasted from seven o'clock until eleven. Five hundred houses were burned and incalculable damage caused. All the leading wine and lumber merchants of San Francisco were ruined. That this fire would lead to renewed building activity & that in this line we might find employment was our general opinion. But this failed to materialize. The majority of merchants that had been burned out were Americans, and the result was that only Americans were engaged for reconstruction purposes.

Having looked in vain for work and not having found employment, Tillier and I concluded to follow the example of one of our countrymen, the Count of Pindray, who owing to his skill had been making a good living.* Now we had long been encouraged in this very move by an old Mexican from San Francisco, a former bear & buffalo hunter named Aluna. So Tillier & I finally decided to unfold to him a plan we had devised of striking out for the prairies, and to ask him to join us in this new venture on which we hoped to embark. He greeted our proposal with obvious pleasure; his advice was to select as the arena of our first exploits the Mariposa and Tulare valleys, regions rich in bear and buffalo. However we begged him to make our novitiate as easy as possible and to

*The Count of Pindray, an impoverished French nobleman, was a famous character in early San Francisco.

begin by hunting less ferocious animals such as elk, deer, goat, hare, rabbit, squirrel, partridges, turtledoves, and blue-jays.

Aluna stood his ground manfully; but in the final analysis since Tillier and I were to supply the funds and he could not make a move without us, he was compelled to accede to our wishes. At length we all agreed that the scene of our hunting activities should be the rolling plains extending from Sonoma to Lake Laguna, and from the ancient Russian colony to the Sacramento.*

Good firearms were what we primarily needed for the career on which we were about to embark. Tillier & I owned excellent guns which had been thoroughly tested when hunting in the Sierra Nevada and at Pine Pass. Next to guns, an indispensable object for our journey was a bark to make bi-weekly trips between Sonoma and San Francisco and from San Francisco to Sonoma. This I went down to the port to select in person. I decided on a boat that was propelled both by sail and oar.

For this purchase I paid 300 piasters, a mere trifle. We then invested in supplies to last a week, carrying these on board together with an ample store of lead & powder. Strange as it may seem, the powder was not costly, the price being the same as in France—that is, four francs the pound. Shot was more valuable; this sold for fifty and sixty centimes.

Now Aluna had an old steed that was still good enough to be taken out hunting, that could carry a man, and also serve as a pack-animal. This saved us a certain amount of expense; so we gratefully accepted the offer he made us. The tent we had just constructed from blankets probably would have

*The Russians first settled on the coast north of San Francisco, at Fort Ross.

proved inadequate in winter; however, as it was now the middle of summer this answered our purpose for this particular season.

On June 26, 1850, we set out after having, at the same price as before, stored our trunks with the German. In my capacity as sailor, upon my shoulders fell the task of piloting our vessel. Tillier and I set out alone on her; Aluna and his horse (for the animal could not be put aboard without causing the boat to capsize) were carried on one of the flat boats, which carry passengers to the mines and which can land at any desired point along the shore. We were to proceed to Sonoma, where the first to arrive were to await for those who came later.

We were the first arrivals; but we were scarcely justified in priding ourselves on our promptness, for no sooner had we pulled our boat upon the sands than we saw Aluna, with his round broad-brimmed hat, his blanket carried in a roll around his body, his trousers split at the sides, and his round vest, coming up at a lively gallop, gun against his hip. Even now the old hunter still made an excellent appearance in this picturesque costume, despite his advanced years.

Although somewhat reluctant to leave our boat pulled up on the bank he appeased us by saying that no one would think of moving it. Inasmuch as he had lived here for twenty years and since he had a far more intimate knowledge of the country than we had, we relied on his past experience. Leaving the boat in the lap of fate, we loaded our tent and supplies on the horse. Our few cooking utensils were packed here and there until we looked more like coppersmiths going out to renew pots and pans, than hunters. Thus loaded we struck out directly across the prairies, traveling from south to north.

XI : HUNTING

WHEN DISCUSSING Captain Sutter's establishment, the fertility of the soil of California was briefly indicated. Especially when reaching the prairies that extend from Sonoma to Santa Rosa was this fertility evident. Frequently the grass through which we were obliged to cut a trail attained a height of nine or ten feet. Along the banks of the Murphy, pines of a thickness and height inconceivable in France were seen. These attain a growth of 200 or 250 feet and are generally 12 or 14 feet in diameter.*

North of San Francisco there existed in 1842 a giant pine. Duflot de Mofras, a noted naturalist who measured it at that date, reported it to be 300 feet high and 60 feet in circumference. In an utterly ruthless manner this dean of the Californian forests was destroyed. Fortunately, however, science

*The traveler refers to the *Sequoia gigantea*, commonly known as the redwood.

assisted in this vandalism and deduced from a number of the concentric layers—each of which represents a year's growth—the age of this giant. Adamson has seen cut down at Senegal a baobab that, according to his measurement, was 25 feet in diameter and, according to his calculation, 6000 years old.*

With a plow such as was used by laborers at the time of Virgil, without harrow and thrasher, the soil of California has produced lavishly. In 1829, the fathers of Mission San José sowed on their lands ten *fanegas* of wheat.† In 1830, 1100 *fanegas*, that is, a return of more than one hundred to one were harvested. The following year they did not plant seed & the soil, lying fallow, still produced 600 *fanegas*. In France, in mediocre soil, wheat returns a yield of two or three to one; in good land, eight or ten; in the best, fifteen or eighteen.

Eighteen months in California are adequate to grow a banana tree. At the age of 18 months the tree fruits and dies; a crop of bananas consists, however, of 160 to 180 fruits weighing from 30 to 40 kilograms.

Mr. Boitard has estimated that a plot of land 100 meters square, planted out to bananas placed two or three meters apart, will produce 2000 kilograms of fruit. By comparison, in the best lands of La Beauce, wheat yields only ten kilograms and potatoes a like yield.

Vineyards have been under cultivation for some time in California. The results have been amazing. Monterey has shipped to San Francisco loads of grapes that rival those

*The trunk of the baobab, the monkey-fruit tree of Africa, often reaches a diameter of thirty feet.
†The *fanega* is approximately 1.60 bushels.

produced in our best vineyards at Fontainebleau. Not only do the plains and forest abound in deer, but the rivers too are stocked with trout and salmon. At certain seasons the coasts and bays, especially the bay of Monterey, present a singular appearance; millions of sardines chased by the hump-back whale attempt to escape from their enemy in shallow waters. Here sea-birds of all kinds, from the frigate-bird to the gull, lie in wait for their prey. The sea at this time resembles a vast bee hive, the air is full of cries and the beating of wings, while off in the distance like moving mountains frolic whales who, having sent the small fish to the sea-birds, wait for the sea-birds to send back their victims.

Out in California the year is divided into two seasons, the dry and the rainy season. The rainy season extends from October through March; the dry season lasts from April to September. There are few cold days during the winter season, the southeast winds that blow during these months tend to temper the climate. The same thing occurs during summer when the northeast breezes cool the burning rays of the sun. In the rainy season, rains fall daily; however, the rains increase from October to January and decrease from February to April. They begin to fall about two o'clock in the afternoon, stopping on toward six o'clock in the evening.

We set out during July, the most delightful time of the year. The temperature varied from 75° to 90° Fahrenheit. From eleven o'clock in the morning to two o'clock in the afternoon this heat made hunting or traveling virtually impossible. What was advisable was to find the welcome shade of pine or oak, & sleep. By way of compensation the afternoons & evenings were delightful. After entering the prairie we began to

hunt; the hunt, however, was to find something for supper.
A few partridges, two or three hares, and some squirrels were
brought down.

Aluna allowed us to do all the hunting without firing; obviously he was conserving his energies for game of greater
importance. He was carrying an English carbine with a single
chamber that used twenty-four balls to the pound. This quite
obviously had seen considerable hard service in his hands.
Originally of flint, the gun had had a piston added at the time
this improvement had first been introduced, and the crude-
ness of the supplementary work contrasted with the good
workmanship of the original rifle.

As we moved on in a leisurely fashion we were just con-
jecturing whether Aluna, of whom we had so often spoken
as a remarkable rifleman, would prove of any use to us except
by supplying a horse when he suddenly stopped and, placing
his hand on my shoulder, made a sign for me to stop. I also
signalled with my finger to Tillier who was a few paces in advance. Everyone remained perfectly quiet. Aluna now placed
his forefinger on his mouth to indicate silence, then waved
his hand in the direction of a small hill that rose on our right.
We looked in vain to ascertain what he was indicating, but
we could see nothing except some twinkling feet flying from
tree to tree, as if gray squirrels were leaping from branch to
branch.

Aluna by shrugging his shoulders warned us in a single
gesture to lie down in the grass; at the same time he led his
horse with the utmost caution into a grove of trees where he
tied him short and where the thick, dense foliage hid him
from sight. Then, removing his poncho, his hat, and even his

vest, he made a detour to get to windward of the animal which he expected to surprise.

We remained behind, literally rooted to the spot, our eyes fixed on the plain he had indicated—a strip of mountain land nearly covered with grass and brush that appeared to be an eight or ten years' growth. About twenty feet away Aluna disappeared through the grass &, although we looked carefully in his direction, yet we heard no noises, and did not even see the tips of the grass move. Neither a snake nor a jackal could have glided or slipped along more silently.

Suddenly we saw above the top of the copse something resembling a dry branch move; then a second branch soon appeared a short distance from the first. Finally in the two parallel objects which had attracted our attention we recognized the horns of a deer. The owner of these horns must have been enormous for, at their tip, the two branches were more than one and one-half meters wide. Perturbed and uneasy, he had raised his head, for a slight gust of wind blowing from our direction that had just passed over him had no doubt warned him of some pending danger.

We lay down on our stomachs flat in the grass. The deer was out of range of our guns; furthermore, we could see only the tip of his head. It was impossible for him to see us but obviously he had had wind of our presence. He moved off from us with nostrils quivering and ears bent forward to catch the slightest sound. Simultaneously a shot like the shot of a pistol was heard. The animal after bounding on for three or four feet then fell down in the underbrush.

We started toward him; but as I have said, we were some 600 or 800 feet away, and the natural obstacles encountered compelled us to make a detour. By the time we reached the small thicket where we had seen him bound off & disappear, this was completely empty except for its mass of aromatic herbs. Then we found him. We looked for the wound; the ball, whose hole was scarcely visible, after grazing the left shoulder had pierced the animal's heart.

Since this was the first deer Tillier and I had seen at close range, we kept looking at it utterly fascinated. The creature was as large as a small horse, and weighed fully 400 pounds. But Aluna merely loaded the animal on his horse with the bored air of a man to whom this was an everyday occurrence.

By now it was almost five o'clock. The spot was ideal for spending the night. A gurgling little brook came down from the mountain only ten paces from where the deer had been dispatched. After unloading the horse I allowed him to graze.

The deer after considerable difficulty was dragged over toward the edge of the stream and was hung by one of his hind feet from the limb of an oak; this fine tree had foliage so thick that in underneath its spreading branches the ground was fairly damp. At the same time Aluna dressed our rabbits, squirrels, and partridges, using the same methods as with the deer, whose liver supplied us with an excellent and bountiful supper. He then urged us to save what game we could not eat; and which might be sold later on at a profit.

In the meantime the tent was being erected, the fire lighted, and the cooking started. The liver of the deer, cooked in fat in the frying pan and seasoned with a glass of wine and a few drops of brandy, made an excellent supper. Since there was still some fresh bread left, the repast was quite complete and when compared to our evening meals at the mines, consisting largely of beans and tortillas, seemed a feast.

Supper over, Aluna proposed that we get some sleep, but we agreed only on condition that we were to be awakened toward midnight to go out hunting with him. One of us, however, had to remain inside the tent to prevent jackals from coming to have a share of our game. Being elated over the results of our hunt, neither Tillier nor I cared to remain behind, so we were forced to draw for the short straw. I was the winner, Tillier being obliged to remain behind and guard the tent.

Wrapping ourselves in our covers we were soon asleep. But this first rest did not last long. Scarcely had darkness descended before we were awakened by the yapping of jackals. Their yell sounded much as if a group of children were being slaughtered. Now & again we had heard their cries when out camping but never in so large a chorus. Drawn by the odor of fresh meat, the precaution taken by Aluna of leaving a guard near our catch was obviously of vital importance.

At midnight we departed, climbing the mountain against the wind, a ruse devised so that game further up would not get wind of us. I asked Aluna for some advice about hunting & what I was expected to do. According to what he reported the deer recently brought down was so large that it was undoubtedly the leader of a herd. By waiting on the banks of the stream we should, according to Aluna, meet the rest of the herd on toward two o'clock in the morning.

Unless deceived about the dead leader's followers, the banks of the stream, according to his belief, would continue to be a good place for all kinds of game. Aluna left me in a small cove in the rocks, stationing himself 100 feet beyond. I crouched down in my recess, passed the ramrod of my gun down its muzzle to make sure the load had not been disturbed &, finding everything in order, sat watching for what might appear.

XII: A NIGHT'S HUNT ON THE PRAIRIES

HUNTERS lying in wait for game invariably observe that during the night, which to man means a time of rest & which he usually spends in sleep, Nature, especially in warm climates, seems fully awake. Merely the type of activity differs. This is characterized by a sense of restlessness, mysteriousness, and pending danger for such members of the animal kingdom as roam abroad. Nyctalops alone seem at their ease for even the rustling wing of the horned-owl, the eagle, the screech-owl, & of the bat breeds mystery; even the step of the wolf, the fox, & the many small carnivorous animals that hunt abroad after dark is furtive & cautious; only the jackal with his incessant howls seems at home in the darkness.

However, to the city-bred man transported to the heart

of the prairies or the forest, these noises are not audible; he fails to hear them, or, if he does hear them, cannot ascertain their origin. But gradually the hunter, who must be able to recognize them, can distinguish these various noises & finally without even seeing the animal can tell who is abroad. Alone in the darkness, although I knew Tillier was in his tent and Aluna barely one hundred steps away, yet I experienced the sensation of complete isolation. So long as man can rely on man, so long as he feels he can give and receive aid, that he has two eyes to see ahead, two eyes to see behind, and four arms for defense, Nature does not seem so overwhelming, so terrible, so hostile, as when he finds himself forced by his own intelligence to forestall danger, to rely on his own eyes to see, on his own strength to fight. Then when his ability to rely on his faculties weakens this confidence in himself disappears; he begins to envy the instinct or sagacity of animals; he longs to be endowed with the ear of a hare to hear, the eye of a lynx to see, the light foot of the tiger-cat that defies detection.

Gradually, man being an animal essentially amenable to education, he acquires all the same characteristics to such a degree that they are a part of his nature; at such a time night no longer seems mysterious; by acquiring such protection against danger he feels a sense of security, for he has now learned a way of defense.

After fifteen days passed out in the prairies under Aluna's tutelage and after suffering to a marked degree all the hopes & fears of a hunter, I was able to distinguish the noise of a snake gliding through the grass, a squirrel leaping from branch to branch, a deer crunching bits of gravel under foot as he went down to drink at a brook. On my first night, however, everything seemed puzzling and I was in constant anguish. I imagined I could see, as I had one night in the Sierra Nevada, the gleaming eyes of a wolf fixed steadily on me, or distinguish the bulky mass of a bear moving in my vicinity.

However, nothing actually happened; for this was a land where bear and other ferocious animals seldom ventured, especially during the summer season. Nevertheless, although hearing loud noises all around me, nothing was visible. Twice or three times I heard the isolated sounds of wild creatures who, whether from caprice or fright passed only ten, fifteen, or twenty feet away. But since they ran off on one side or behind me and so were not within range of vision, merely the noise resounded.

Then out of the silence was heard the clear, ringing report of Aluna's rifle. Suddenly sounds were heard in every direction; then I heard what seemed like the gallop of a horse approaching. In an instant, over on the opposite side of the stream, passed an animal of enormous size, on whom I fired at random. To appease my conscience, I fired twice. Then I remained motionless, as if petrified by the report of the very rifle I was holding. Almost immediately was heard a low whistle; from this I realized that Aluna wanted me to come to his assistance.

After ascending the banks of the brook, I discovered him engaged in performing on a hind the identical operation he had performed on the deer. Both the doe & buck had been struck on the same spot and had apparently succumbed at once to the wound. Aluna now asked me what I had fired on, so I told him about the huge animal that had rushed past. From my description Aluna was of the belief that my two shots had been fired at an elk.

There was no chance of accomplishing anything more that night. Our two shots seemed to have aroused every creature on the plains and, once intimidated, they would never be imprudent enough to return. Having made a kind of bed of branches, on this our doe was placed; then each of us took hold of one of her hind feet and, pulling this bed of branches along with the animal in order to save the hide, which was used for very fine saddles, we began to drag her toward our tent.

We found Tillier up and waiting for us. He had not once closed his eyes, having passed all the evening scaring off jackals, who seemed to have congregated from all the far corners of the prairie to attack our game. Several had even fallen on the remains of the deer which we had thrown about twenty feet from our tent. That they had found their quarry was soon known by the joyful yaps of those who had located this welcome feast, for they seemed to be laughing at the disappointed yells of their famished companions.

The hunt had been successful and was enough to warrant a trip back to San Francisco. A deer, a doe, four rabbits, four squirrels, and two crested partridges had been caught. So Tillier and I planned to leave at once for San Francisco in order to market our game. Aluna remained behind to look after our tent and to attempt in our absence to kill, insofar as possible, a large number of buck and doe.

After considerable difficulty the deer and doe were packed on the back of our horse; we then added by way of ornament the hares, rabbits, squirrels, and partridges. Shortly before dawn we took the road toward San Francisco Bay. By not losing any time, at four o'clock we were in the city. While returning to San Francisco there was no difficulty in tracing the path over which we had come just the evening before. Our route was clearly defined over the prairie just as, in the morning, the traces of dog and hunter returning from the night's hunt may be readily distinguished in the clover. Before leaving I suggested that Aluna go over to the locality where I had fired my shots and see whether there were any traces of blood. I had fired at such close range that I felt that despite my excitement I could scarcely have missed.

The morning was crisp and delightful; never had Tillier and I felt so carefree and light-hearted. In the independent life of the hunter there is joy and satisfaction akin to that of complete freedom. Toward five o'clock in the morning we stopped for something to eat. We had brought along some bread that had been hollowed out and where the crumbs had been removed we had placed what remained of the liver of our deer; in addition we had a flask filled with brandy and water. This was a repast fit for a prince.

While lunching under a green oak and while our horse fully loaded was munching some twigs from a shrub of which he was especially fond, we sighted a dozen vultures which were circling about in a strange manner. Their band was rapidly increasing and from twelve their number soon increased to twenty or twenty-five. From their course they seemed to be following the trail across the prairie of some animal who, from time to time, was compelled to stop. At such times they too would stop, ascend, then come down & nearly alight on the ground; the next instant they would fly off as if frightened.

Obviously off on the prairie about one quarter of a league away, something out of the ordinary was occurring. Taking my gun and orientating myself, to avoid getting lost, by means of a clump of oaks from which towered tall pines that resembled an immense tower, I moved quietly across the prairie. There was no danger of going astray. I had merely to raise my eyes & the thieving vultures would serve as guides.

The scavengers became more and more agitated; from various points along the horizon more birds of the same species swiftly congregated. There was something stupendous about the force & power of this flight which was rapid as a cannon shot for, once under way, the birds moved without apparent effort. Upon arriving at the congested area each scavenger seemed to succumb to the general feeling of curiosity; and to prepare to play his part, in so far as possible, in the drama that was taking place, or about to be enacted. Since the flight of the vultures, once they were united, was not rapid & since they merely flew here & there among the crowd flying alternately up and down, I gained steadily on them. Suddenly this flapping movement ceased; they became almost motionless, gave shrill cries, fluttered their wings, and then made a concerted movement. By now I was nearly 100 feet from the spot where at any moment they seemed about to strike.

Here the prairie was at its thickest; even by raising up on my tiptoes my head was barely on a level with the grass; but I was guided, as I have said, by the band of robbers. Gradually I moved on ahead. Off in another direction I perceived Tillier standing up in a tree and calling to me from afar in words that I could not distinguish, at the same time making gestures that I could not understand. From where he was standing he seemed to be able to see what was going on, and toward this by cries and gestures he was attempting to pilot me. Being only some 500 paces away from the scene of activities, I continued on ahead, gun in hand, prepared to fire in an emergency.

When I had taken about twenty steps I seemed to hear groans, then the sounds that accompany a desperate combat; at the same time the thieves rose, turned, and then flew down with cries of fury. From all appearances a thief had unexpectedly closed in on their prey which they were already regarding as their own exclusive property. Upon hearing this noise and these groans which seemed quite near at hand, I redoubled my precautions &, moving constantly ahead, was soon aware that I was only separated from the scene of this struggle, whatever this might be, by a comparatively short distance.

Quietly moving over the last obstacle and crawling like an adder I reached the edge of the grass. An animal whose species I did not at first glance recognize was crouching ten feet away from me, still moving in the last throes of agony, & serving as a kind of barrier to conceal some man of whom I could perceive only the tip of the gun and the top of the head. The man, with eye fixed on the spot where I should soon appear, was prepared to fire when I advanced.

Gun, head, intense eye, all this I recognized in a single, comprehensive glance. Suddenly jumping up I cried: 'Oh, Father Aluna, don't be foolish. Good heavens, it is I!' 'I rather thought so,' replied Aluna, lowering his gun; 'so much the better, you can come and help me. But first fire off your gun at all these brawlers and squawkers hanging around, or they will not give us a moment's quiet.' With these words he indicated the scavengers shrieking overhead. I fired into the thick of the flock; one robber flopped over. By now the others had flown off out of gun range; however, they were not inclined to let us out of their sight. From Aluna I begged an explanation of how we had happened to meet.

The coincidence was quite simple. In accordance with my suggestions he had gone at daybreak to examine the place where I had fired on my elk, and here, just as I had expected, found my animal had apparently been wounded, a fact relatively easy to trace from the trail of blood left in his flight. So Aluna started off at once to follow this blood trail.

With the keen knowledge of a hunter he soon recognized that the animal was not only wounded, but had wounds in two places—the neck and the hind leg. The wounds were in the neck because branches, at the height of six feet, bore traces of blood; and in the hind-quarters, for when the elk crossed a sandy stretch, Aluna found on the sand only the marks of three feet. He knew then that the fourth, in place of touching the ground, was dragging, for this left on the ground a kind of irregular ridge, all covered with clots of blood. Assuming that, thus crippled, the animal could not travel far, he had started off in pursuit.

Approximately at the end of a league he had found the grass trampled down and heavily stained with blood where the animal, exhausted by his wounds, had been forced to stop for a brief respite. Only at the approach of Aluna had he pulled himself up and gone on. And so the scavengers, as is their custom when an animal is wounded out on the prairie, were following him until he fell.

Of this flight, not being versed like Aluna in the mysteries of the chase, I could not surmise the cause; however, this had guided me as it had also guided him. Unluckily for these scavengers at the very moment when, lacking strength to go further, the victim was about to fall and just as they were ready to pounce on him & tear him to pieces when still alive, Aluna had arrived on the spot and to avoid wasting a charge of powder, had cut his hamstring. This was what had caused the scolding noises which I had recognized but of whose meaning I was ignorant. Our hunt was now increased by meat that alone weighed as much as all the rest combined.

XIII : SNAKE-GRASS

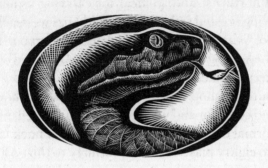

THERE WAS no possible way of loading this new burden on our poor, overloaded horse; he was carrying everything he was able to carry. But off in the distance was seen a *carreta* bound from Santa Rosa to Sonoma.* This belonged to one of the rancheros. Finally a bargain was struck with him whereby for two piasters he was to allow us to load our game in his *carreta* and would himself aid us in its transportation.

That evening he was returning to Santa Rosa & so would bring back our horse whose pack, upon arriving in Sonoma, would be placed on the boat. Aluna now set off along the route where he expected to find good hunting. Accompanied by Tillier we continued on our journey. By one o'clock that

*The *carreta*, a wooden cart drawn by oxen, was used to transport produce in California.

[105]

same afternoon we were in Sonoma. As our boat was lying upon the bank, with the aid of some citizens of Sonoma we transferred our game aboard her. Fortunately the wind was from the northeast and so ideal for carrying us across the bay. Having hoisted sail, within three hours we reached San Francisco. As it was now four o'clock in the afternoon I rushed over to the leading butcher, leaving Tillier to guard our game which was protected with leaves and grass.

This butcher-shop was run by an American, whom I told what I had come for and what game had just been unloaded. Under normal conditions in San Francisco a buck is valued at sixty to eighty piasters; a doe, at thirty to thirty-five piasters; a hare at six or eight; a crested partridge at one piaster; and a squirrel at one-half piaster. There was no fixed price for elk. I am of the belief that this was the first elk to be sold to the San Francisco market. We agreed on a lump sum and, in exchange for over 500 pounds of meat, received 300 piasters.

That same evening we departed. By rowing vigorously we pulled in to Sonoma about one o'clock in the morning, then lay down in the bottom of our boat & slept until five o'clock. Soon we were again under way to rejoin Aluna. This time we veered somewhat to the right following the east slope of a small chain of hills where the grass was considerably lower than down on the plains and where, as a result, hunting was less arduous.

Seven or eight doe soon appeared. We managed to kill two of them. Now we had carefully observed the operation Aluna performed after their death, an operation more necessary in a warm climate like California than in other countries. So we selected some branches of oaks having unusually thick foliage to keep our doe fresh, then suspended them from branches high enough to prevent jackals from getting at them. By eleven o'clock we were again in camp.

Upon our arrival we saw a doe and a buck hanging from the limb of an oak. Aluna in the meantime had apparently not been idle. Then as the heat was quite intense we concluded he must be taking a siesta and so looked around very quietly. He was in fact sleeping soundly.

But something else rolled up on his poncho was sleeping with him, something that brought terror to our hearts. For here was a rattlesnake that had come over to enjoy the warmth and softness of his woolen blanket. Aluna happened to be sleeping on his right side. But if he were to turn over in his sleep onto his left side, and by so doing crush the snake into the ground, the snake would be sure to strike. Tillier and I stood motionless on the threshold of the tent scarcely daring to breathe, with our eyes glued on this deadly reptile, not knowing what to do. At the slightest sound Aluna might move; to move might mean death.

Finally we decided to remove this deadly sleeping companion, for the snake, too, seemed lost in slumber. Aluna's position has already been described; he was sleeping on his right side rolled up in his poncho. The reptile had glided close to him, in fact his tail and the lower end of his body were hidden inside the folds of his coat. Some of the upper end was so twisted as to resemble the coils of a heavy cable, while the head was folded under the neck as if asleep.

Tillier, by circling around past Aluna's head, came over to the other side and by thrusting the barrel of his gun within the coil made by the sleeping snake, stood ready with a single rapid thrust to throw him far off to one side. In the meantime I had drawn out a kind of hunting knife I usually carried in a belt and stood by ready to cut the snake in half. I now signalled to Tillier that I was ready. Immediately with the gun that served as a kind of spring the serpent was lifted and hurled against the canvas wall of our tent. Not expecting him to alight there, I failed to get him with my hunting knife when he landed. The serpent coiled himself, rattling ominously, and I can assure you that when I saw his dull eye glow like a red ruby & his livid mouth fall wide open, my blood froze.

The commotion had, however, awakened Aluna. At first he may not have understood why Tillier had his gun and I my knife; but after one brief glance at the snake the situation was obvious. 'Ah, you earthworm!' he exclaimed, with a scorn impossible to convey. Then stretching out his long arm he seized the serpent by the tail and whistling as he swung it around two or three times, as a slinger swings a rope, knocked its head against one of the stakes of our tent.

Then, with a disdainful gesture he threw it off about twenty feet, went away, walked down to the stream, washed his hands, wiped them on some oak leaves, and coming back to us remarked, 'Well, did you make a good sale?' Tillier and I were as white as sheets. Tillier handed him our pouch. Aluna after counting the piasters divided them into three equal portions, then with obvious satisfaction placed his 100 piasters in a leather pouch that hung from his belt. Dating from this episode, Aluna in the eyes of both Tillier and myself won the respect he merited.

There was still another phase of it; that is, we did not take into consideration the part played by habit. Quite possibly at the beginning of his nomadic life he too may have been somewhat timid; perhaps the sight of his first snake had frightened him even more than it had us; but habit is a powerful lever. From habit anything becomes familiar, even death itself.

In fact, in his travels east, he had explored lands unknown even at the present day that lie between the two routes followed by caravans, regions extending from Lake Pyramid to St. Louis, Missouri, and from Monterey to Santa Fé. In these extensive regions where rivers, lacking outlets, disappear in the sands or terminate in salt-impregnated lagoons and marshes, lands carrying bitumen and crossed only by men & animals who are equally untamed, Aluna had grown accustomed to every kind of peril.

This is the way Aluna came to know rattlers. One evening, near the left bank of the Colorado River in the land of the Navajo Indians, after indicating the trail to two missionaries and an Englishman who were lost, Aluna, who had a loathing for beaten routes, galloped off on his horse across the prairie. Reaching on the banks of a stream a location that seemed suitable for spending the night, Aluna unrolled his buffalo-skin and arranged his saddle as carefully as a housewife prepares sleeping quarters. To broil a few slices of deer, as well as to keep off ferocious animals during the night, he lighted a fire, first taking the precaution, however, to pull out all the grass around the place used for a hearth to avoid setting fire to the prairies.

After the fire was started and the deer-steak cooking over the coals, Aluna was afraid he might run short of wood during the night. Observing a large pine on the far side of the creek, he took out his Mexican knife & started out to lay in a supply. In a single leap he reached the far side of the brook. But upon alighting his feet touched something alive. Aluna tumbled over backwards.

Then he saw rising from the grass the head of a rattle-snake; simultaneously from a sharp pain in the knee he was aware that the serpent had just struck. His first feeling was one of rage. Hurling himself on the reptile, Aluna with his Mexican knife cut the viper into three or four segments. However, he was wounded; undoubtedly mortally wounded. To go out and cut down wood to keep the fire burning was now useless, long before the fire would be out, Aluna would be dying.

Sad & dejected he retraced his steps &, offering up a prayer which he believed would be his last prayer on earth, sat down again near his fire; even now he believed he could distinguish throughout his body a cold numb feeling. As he sat preparing for death to overtake him, with leg already numb, swollen, inflamed and turning blue, he suddenly remembered—and Aluna never doubted that it was in answer to his prayer that this remedy had been sent—he suddenly remembered, I say, that in clearing out the grass around his fire he had torn out large bunches of what the Indians call snake-grass.

Making a supreme effort he dragged himself over to the spot where he recalled having seen this herb. Here, in fact, were two or three feet of the root Aluna had extracted. Washing and cleaning his knife, for it was still slimy and thick with blood and masticating some of the roots to save time, he broke the remaining grass into small pieces, which he put to boil in a silver cup that had just been given him by the Englishmen as compensation for his services in finding their road for them. Then, since he had heard the savages describe innumerable times what to do, he applied the crushed roots to the open wound on his leg. This was the first dressing.

In the meanwhile the root boiling in the cup was forming a dark-green liquid which emitted a strongly alkaline odor. Under normal conditions this drink would have been unbearable to swallow. Aluna, however, diluted it with water and despite his repugnance drank the entire amount. This act saved his life. No sooner had he drunk this liquid than dizziness overcame him; the ground seemed to move, the sky turned livid overhead, the moon which was just rising seemed like an enormous head that had been wounded and was sweating blood.

He gave a long sigh believing the end was near, and fell down motionless on his bison-robe. At dawn the following morning Aluna was awakened by his horse who, not knowing the cause of his master's profound slumber, was licking his face. Upon awakening he could not at first recall what had occurred. He experienced a general feeling of weakness, with dull pains and great lassitude. A semi-paralysis seemed to have spread throughout the lower half of his body. Then he remembered what had happened.

With acute anxiety he pulled his wounded leg toward him, rolled up his trousers and looked at the wound under the bandage of crushed roots which he had fastened around his leg with his handkerchief. The wound was red and the leg only slightly inflamed. He now renewed the operation of the previous evening and crushed more of the healing root; this time, however, despite its alkaline odor, despite its flavor of turpentine, he eagerly seized & drank the juice. Next a new bandage was applied to replace the old.

After this, lacking strength to reach shade, he slipped under his buffalo robe. There, perspiring profusely, he remained until three o'clock that afternoon. By three o'clock he felt strong enough to go over to the stream to bathe his leg and drink a few mouthfuls of fresh water.

Although his head still felt heavy & his pulse was beating feverishly, Aluna realized he was improving. He called to his horse, who came at his master's order, put on a saddle, rolled up his buffalo-robe, took a supply of snake-grass &, climbing with considerable effort up into the saddle, rode over toward a Navajo village some five or six leagues away.

Here lived some natives with whom he was on friendly terms and by whom he was warmly received. An old Indian nursed his wound and as he was already well on the road to recovery, this wound soon healed. From then on Aluna invariably regarded a rattlesnake bite like any ordinary accident; however, he always carried in a small skin pouch some of the grass & the healing root, replenishing these whenever the opportunity afforded.

XIV : ALUNA

ALUNA often said, as he raised his head with a certain melancholy movement, 'How foolish I once was!' We never knew to what folly he referred. I personally believe and, despite evidence to the contrary, persisted in my belief that for Aluna these words, 'How foolish I once was,' simply had reference to a time when he was in love. From other bits of conversation dropped in the course of our long evening chats I was led to believe, as I have just said, that once Aluna had been in love and, having lost the woman he loved, had become so morose that his conduct had bordered on folly. But how had he lost her? This was a point that invariably remained a mystery, for as Aluna never made any definite remarks on the subject, I can speak only from inference.

At the time Aluna had conducted himself so foolishly he was living near the Wind River Mountains along the banks of the Arkansas River, where he had decided to build a cabin. But why had this cabin, so enthusiastically begun, not been finished? Why had it remained in a state of incompletion and fastened only by shutters, by a door with a simple latch? Had Aluna perhaps come to realize one day that he might have to live all alone in a house that was begun for two & so from that time on had but little interest in whether the house remained open or closed after the only thing he believed worthy of bolts and locks disappeared?

One evening after a long absence he came in and found a door he had expected to find closed standing ajar. He believed he could see where a pile of corn which had been stacked in one corner of the cabin and which had reached almost to the ceiling had greatly diminished. Although he did not value this supply of corn highly, and would gladly have shared this at any time with any neighbor who might have asked for it, yet Aluna did not like to have anyone take what he owned without first informing him, for in this loss he saw not only the actual robbery but also evidence of what seemed like scorn on the part of the thief toward his victim.

Under such circumstances the robbery put Aluna in bad humor. Now the culprit had left the door open and with the expectation of returning had evidently made himself quite at home. So Aluna lay down, keeping a kind of hatchet that was used for carpenter work close at hand. With his Mexican knife thrust in his belt, he awaited the thief.

But for Aluna, as for all men engaged in active work, sleep, even if only for short periods, is absolutely imperative. As a result, no matter how much Aluna tried to keep awake, he dozed off occasionally. In the middle of the night he awakened with the feeling that someone was boldly stealing his pile of corn, for the dry leaves were crackling in a way to indicate that the visitor had no intention of keeping quiet.

The thief, so it seemed, had not even taken the trouble to come over to the bed, but in the belief that Aluna was always absent, had begun noisily to forage in the pile of corn. To Aluna this seemed absolutely brazen, and he called out in Spanish, 'Who's there?' The noise stopped, but no one answered. Aluna jumped out of bed and, as the robber failed to reply, repeated his question in the Indian dialect. But the question met with no more success in one language than in the other. This silence proved annoying.

The individual in the cabin, whoever he might be, apparently intended to leave as he had entered, that is, incognito. He even seemed to walk with slow and heavy feet, like a man who fears to be overheard, although from time to time his breathing, over which he apparently lacked control, revealed his presence. Aluna was even inclined to believe that these steps instead of approaching the door were approaching him. Of this he soon had no doubt; the robber, hoping to surprise him, was advancing toward the recess which he used as an alcove. Aluna now prepared to put up a fight.

Since this gave evidence of being a hand to hand conflict, he grasped his knife in his left hand, his hatchet in his right & waited. Soon he felt rather than saw that his adversary was only about two feet away. Reaching out his hand, he touched a rough and shaggy coat. All doubt now vanished; his robber was a bear.

Aluna recoiled quickly; but behind him was the wall that prevented him from moving backward. No matter what his inclination was, there was no recourse left but to fight. Now Aluna was not a man to back down; moreover, as he himself observed, at this time he was almost insane, danger was a matter of indifference, & so he had no regrets about terminating his span of life. Raising up the arm that held the hatchet, he brought it down with full force at random, trusting to providence where it would hit. The hatchet fell on one of the bear's paws, inflicting a large wound. As the full force of the blow was felt, the bear, no longer silent, burst forth in a hideous roar of agony. With his other paw he caught Aluna in the flank, pulling him toward him.

Aluna had barely time, by slipping his hand under the bear's paw, to press the handle of his knife against his Mexican cartridge belt. As a result the more the bear clutched Aluna tightly against his body, the more the knife was forced of its own accord into the brute's chest. In the meanwhile, with his right hand Aluna kept striking the bear's nose with the iron-clad handle of his hatchet.

The bear, however, is an animal with an extraordinarily tough hide, and it took him some time to realize that he was stabbing himself by closely hugging Aluna. Just as the latter was beginning to find the embrace too arduous, by good luck the knife penetrated his vital organs. Instantly the bear uttered a shriek of rage, hurling Aluna away from him. Thrown with a violence more terrific than he had ever experienced, Aluna might have been flattened out against the wall. But by accident he fell through the open door and rolled out about ten paces beyond. In the struggle Aluna had, unfortunately, lost his hatchet, and as he had left his knife in the bear's stomach he was now unarmed.

Luckily, near enough to be reached was an oak stake, pointed like a sword, that had been prepared along with several others to form an enclosure around the house. Against this stake Aluna had been thrown. As he arose, although somewhat exhausted from the struggle, he took hold of it. In the hands of a vigorous man like Aluna, this weapon was as deadly as a club in the hands of Hercules.

This he soon had occasion to use, for the animal, infuriated at the double wound, followed him menacingly from the cabin. Though not tenacious of life, yet Aluna did not propose to die in so harsh a manner as that which threatened as the maddened animal raged toward him. Mustering every ounce of strength to meet what might prove a mortal combat, he rained on the bear a shower of blows heavy enough to break a bull's back.

But the bear, with all the adroitness of a fencer, warded off most of the blows as they fell, attempting constantly to seize the stake and wrest it from Aluna's hand. Had it not been for his wounded paw he would have succeeded immediately, although in the end he won out. Now that the stake had been caught by the animal Aluna made no effort to resist and merely let go his hold, which was released at the very moment when the bear was about to inflict a violent blow. The bear, expecting him to resist, fell over backward. Aluna, taking advantage of this brief respite to rush into his house, quickly closed the door behind him. But the bear had no intention of allowing him to escape. By throwing the full force of his weight against the door just as Aluna was closing it, man and beast, separated only by the door that had finally pulled off its hinges, rolled over into the room.

As he fell Aluna put his hand on his missing hatchet and, using this and one of his arms for a shield, lifted up the door behind which he took refuge. At the same time the bear, just as Aluna had expected, also caught hold of the door with his two paws. Aluna then released his hold and, bringing down the hatchet that he fortunately carried, wounded the animal on the other paw.

Injured now in both front paws and with a knife buried deep in his chest the bear, finally aware that the odds were against him, began to consider trying to retreat. Aluna had by this time manoeuvered in such a way that he could reach his gun, which up until now he had been unable to use. With this finally in hand, he leaped up, cocked the gun, and placed it across the entrance. While thus engaged, the moon peered out from the clouds as if to aid Aluna by enabling him to see what he was doing. The bear seemed to hesitate for a time as if trying to decide whether to leave the house; then with a thundering growl started over toward the door.

Aluna now barricaded the entrance, gun in hand. But the bear still had strength enough to fight, according to his habit, at close range. Aluna, alert to his every movement, stepped back and fired, aiming at the side opposite to where the knife had entered. The bear, recoiling some two paces, fell over backward with a heavy thud. The ball had pierced his heart.

Despite the fact that this bear was black, he was nearly as tall as a gray bear and weighed 800 pounds. Had Aluna, on the other hand, met a grizzly bear, instead of having to combat a black one, the affair might have terminated in quite another manner. The gray bear uses both teeth and claws in a fight whereas the black bear, on the contrary, does not use them. The latter merely attempts to seize his enemy in his clutches, squeeze him against his body, and crush him with his powerful grip. What hunting buck, doe, and deer was to a man accustomed to such dangerous hunting as has just been narrated, can be readily understood.

Aluna had many other narrow escapes as well so that by comparison what he faced with us seemed of minor importance. These dangers had left their definite impress on him; nevertheless, he spoke of them without emotion, being invariably ready to face them again without hesitating, should the occasion arise.

But of his adventures along the Colorado River and in the swamps of Eastern Texas, where he had had two horses devoured by alligators and monsters, he spoke with deeper feeling. Now an alligator is quite familiar to us all; but I question whether scholars or even naturalists have ever heard of a *carvana*. For my part I hesitate to say that a *carvana* may perhaps have existed merely in Aluna's imagination. Be this as it may, a *carvana* was to this intrepid man what an old bogey is to very young children.

This monster lives, so it seems, in Eastern Texas out in those vast marshes that present on the surface the appearance of solid ground, but which are actually nothing more than vast lakes of slime, where in a few seconds horse and rider founder. Through these treacherous dungeons of death exist, however, a few trails marked by thick growth of reeds. These trails are known only to the Indians and local inhabitants. But how are they known? This is what they themselves would probably find difficult to explain; the lone traveler, who has no possible way of locating these narrow causeways, is invariably lost in the marshes.

In addition, still another danger exists. Here and there off on the prairies, grow small clumps of brambles measuring fifteen or twenty feet in circumference. If the traveler before proceeding observes closely, he recoils in fright, for coiled in these bushes may be seen the bodies of myriads of snakes unknown to the prairies, which dwell only on these leafy islands. These reptiles are the water-moccasin, the brown viper, & the red-headed black snake, three serpents whose bite is fatal & more rapid perhaps in its effects than that of the rattler. Even so, the traveler bitten by them is more fortunate than the man who is a victim of the alligator's tail or the teeth of a *carvana*.

Now these two monsters have their haunts, as already indicated, in these beds of slime. A horse losing its foothold is immediately doomed; with eye aflame he strugggles for an instant with bristling mane and nostrils quivering in the mire where he cannot swim; then suddenly shuddering gives a feeble quiver, as he finally feels himself being drawn down by some irresistible force into an abyss. Gradually he disappears, struggling against some hidden enemy. Of this monster all that is visible is a crooked tail, bristling with rough scales that glisten through the mud. An alligator's attack and defense is made by the use of this enormous tail which, curving in a semi-circle doubles back to his jaws.

Unfortunate is the man who, through imprudence or chance crosses the path of this hideous tail! This dangerous animal strikes with his tail whatever he wishes to devour, then pushes it toward the jaws which, as soon as the tail begins to move, open to their full capacity while the head turns to one side ready to receive what the tail is sending and which is instantaneously crushed by these hideous and deadly jaws.

From this same alligator, however, the planters of Texas, New Mexico, and the neighboring regions secure fat which is used to grease the wheels of their mills. During the season for hunting alligators, that is, about the middle of autumn, these animals seem to come & surrender of their own accord. Leaving their muddy lakes and slimy rivers they now emerge to seek warmer winter quarters. In so doing they dig holes under the roots of trees, then bury themselves underground. At this season they also gorge themselves to such an extent that they are no longer dangerous. The negroes who hunt them at this time of year cut the tail from the balance of the body with a single blow of the hatchet, and yet even this terrific impact scarcely arouses them.

This first step accomplished, the alligators are then cut into pieces which are thrown into immense caldrons where, as fast as the water boils, the fat rises to the surface. This a negro collects with a large spoon. Ordinarily only one man is needed for the triple task of killing the alligator, boiling it, and extracting the fat. Negroes, so it is said, often kill as many as fifteen alligators in a single day. There is no record of them receiving, at this time of the year, the slightest scratch.

As for the *carvana*, that is quite another story. This monster is far more destructive, far more dangerous, than the alligator at its worst. However, none has been seen alive. Nor is the monster of any apparent value, even if he should appear. But when lagoons dry up, or after the rivers change their channels, dead *carvanas* have been found, and are known to resemble gigantic tortoises with shells ten or twelve feet long & six feet wide. The head and tail are like those of an alligator. Hiding in the mud much as the ant-lion hides in the sands, he awaits his prey in the center of a kind of tunnel with jaws constantly open to seize what victim fate sends across his path. Twice Aluna barely escaped these deadly monsters by abandoning his horse that disappeared, ground between invisible jaws in which he had heard bones crack.

One day, however, some officers of an American engineering corps who were measuring distances between New Mexico & New Orleans, saw one of their comrades fall into the jaws of a *carvana*, and so determined, together with an American planter with whom they were boarding and where Aluna was also staying, to extricate the monster, no matter at what cost, from the deep abyss where he was hiding. So for this strange fishing expedition the following preparations were completed.

The anchor of a small boat was attached to a chain thirty or forty feet long; to this anchor a lamb about two weeks old was attached for bait. The anchor and lamb were then thrown down into the mud, the far end of the chain being bound around the base of a tree. Here a negro was stationed to guard this strange line that had been cast overboard.

The following day the negro came running to say that the *carvana* was dead, and that the shaking he had given to the anchor which he had in all probability swallowed had been felt on the chain, and was causing the tree to shake. Since it was too late to attempt to land the *carvana* that evening there was no alternative but to await until morning to pull the monster up from his slimy retreat.

At dawn the following day all met at the rendezvous. The chain was found to have been strained to such an extent that the bark of the tree around which it was wrapped had been cut as if by a saw. Some ropes were quickly tied to the chain and to these ropes were yoked two horses. Although these horses were lashed and whipped, yet their combined efforts proved ineffectual to pull the *carvana* from the abyss. In fact, no sooner would they take a step in advance than some irresistible force pulled them back.

At length, aware that these horses were making no headway, the farmer sent out for the two strongest oxen on his farm. These were now yoked up with the horses & also urged to pull. For a time some hope was entertained that their efforts might bear fruit; for a moment the surface of the slime was shaken by a submarine trembling, as the tip of the animal's jaws appeared. Suddenly the anchor, pulled violently away, rebounded from the swamps upon the banks.

Of the flukes of the anchor one was broken; the other, badly twisted, warped, and battered, carried with it bits of flesh and bone torn from the jaws of the monster. But the creature remained invisible, and from the manner in which the mud was agitated, the inference was that he was lying far down in the depths of the abyss. Of such a character were the hideous monsters that had inspired such horror in the mind of our comrade Aluna, yet the feeling he exhibited in speaking of these almost mythical creatures was tinged more with disgust than with fear.

Another day he was traveling along the Rocky Mountains between their base and a lake which had not as yet been named by any traveler. Here Aluna was chased by a troop of shaggy Indians. Now the cock of his gun was broken and, as he felt his horse give way under him and realized that with fresh horses the Indians must eventually overtake him, he concluded to take advantage of the fact that darkness was falling to escape by a subterfuge to which he had promised himself to resort when in such a predicament.

This subterfuge was quite simple; he merely lashed his horse forcing him to continue on riderless and to keep to the road. The result was that the more the Indians gained on the horse who, relieved of his rider, now redoubled his speed and made headway, the further they would be carried away from their victim.

So, heading toward a small pine forest and having already removed his stirrups, the instant he passed under one of these trees he seized a strong branch and held on, while the horse continued on ahead. Aluna then pulled his feet up on the same limb to which he was held only by his hands, and in a second climbed up into the tree. A dozen savages passed at a lively gallop below. Aluna both saw and heard them, but not an Indian caught a glimpse of Aluna. When they were far away and when the noise of their galloping horses was no longer distinguishable, Aluna came down and looked around for a place in which to pass the night.

Within a few moments he found one of those caverns so frequently found at the base of the Rocky Mountains; this led into a vast and spacious cavern, one which, however, was full of gloom, being lighted only by the passage Aluna had discovered. Gliding in like a snake, Aluna searched for and finally found a large stone which he rolled against the aperture so that no one, either man or beast, would attempt to come in after him. Rolling up in his poncho, and being worn out as he was by fatigue, he was soon sound asleep.

So profoundly did Aluna sleep, especially in the beginning, that he had difficulty in waking up enough to find out what was happening down near his feet. Such sounds as cats frequently make sharpening their claws on a broom, one or more animals with unusually sharp claws was making on Aluna's legs.

Aluna, raising his head to convince himself he was not dreaming, put his hand down & felt two baby jaguars about the size of large cats who, attracted no doubt by the odour of fresh meat, were toying with Aluna's legs, and scratching around with their claws where the slits up the sides of his trousers left his leg exposed. He immediately realized that he had entered a cave that was the retreat of a jaguar and her young; that the mother and father were probably off hunting and would soon return and that, as a result, the only thing to do was to leave immediately. Snatching his gun and rolling up his poncho, he started to push back the stone, abandon the refuge he had discovered, and move on out into the open.

But the moment he laid his hand on the stone he heard, less than 100 paces away, a low growl that warned him he was too late, & that the female had returned. Another growl barely twenty feet away told him she was returning at full speed. Simultaneously he could feel against the stone the pressure of the animal attempting to come into her cave to her young. The little ones, on their part, answered the mothers's growls by a kind of soft whimpering full of impatient threats.

Aluna had his gun; but, as has been said, the cock was broken, making this part of the gun useless. Aluna, however, devised a way to make it of service. Placing his back against the stone to keep it in position, despite the efforts of the jaugar he began to load his gun as rapidly as possible. Simple as was this operation under ordinary conditions, it was complicated at this time by a highly unpleasant disturbance.

Two feet away, behind the stone that kept moving every moment by the force of her pressure, roared the female jaugar. He could feel her powerful breath at close range whenever she thrust her head in the crevices left open at points where the stone was badly joined to the wall. Once he even felt her paw reaching in on his shoulder. But nothing swerved Aluna from the important operation he was accomplishing. Having loaded his gun, Aluna struck the steel to ignite a spark from the flint. At each spark that flew off the stone he glanced around the cave all strewn with the bones of animals devoured by the two jaguars; among these bones were the two young jaguars who looked at him & jumped as each spark was struck.

In the meanwhile the mother continued to storm against the stone blocking the entrance. Aluna had however loaded his gun, and lighted his flint; his turn to be the aggressor had now come. Turning around and keeping in so far as possible the weight of his body against the stone, he then pointed the barrel of his carbine through the crack where the jaguar's head and paw had appeared.

Watching this strange object approach and threaten her, the jaguar finally seized it with her teeth, attempting to crush it as she would a bone. This was the very indiscretion on which Aluna had counted. Approaching the loaded gun with his bit of lighted tinder, he fired off the shot. The jaguar swallowed the entire charge—lead, powder, and fire. A smothered roar followed by a cry of agony warned Aluna that his enemy had been conquered. He could now breath freely again.

The truce proved to be only short-lived. As he got up from

his knees a new roar, more terrible than the last, was heard. This was the male jaguar who had come running at the cries of his mate. Unfortunately he arrived too late to unite his efforts with hers; but he did arrive in time to cause Aluna more anxiety. Inasmuch as Aluna had been so successful with his first experiment he had no thought of adopting any other mode of attack. So he prepared to handle the old male just as he had handled his mate. With this end in view he leaned his back up against the stone and began again to reload his gun.

The jaguar had paused an instant near his dead mate and roared pathetically. Then, the funeral oration over, he hurled himself against the stone. Aluna, from within, replied by a grunt that might perhaps be interpreted as follows: 'Come on, my good friend, come on, before long we shall chat over our little affairs in person!'

In fact, with his gun loaded Aluna was on the point of striking his flint when he discovered that in the rather hasty movements he had just made he had lost his tinder-box. His situation was extremely grave; without a tinder, no fire; without a fire, no means of defense. The carbine, reduced to its simplest terms, was nothing more than an iron tube that as a last resort might serve as a club, and nothing more.

Aluna felt in vain with his hands to the right and left, but could not locate it. He searched futilely with his feet among whatever was within reach, but his foot touched only stones & bones. All this time, against the stone were being directed some severe thrusts; the jaguar breathing noisily even reached out now and again with his paw and touched the shoulder of the hunter from whose forehead drops of sweat began to pour. Were these caused by impatience, or by fear? Aluna, who was very frank, swore that it came from both causes. Recognizing at length that his search was futile, he now knew that, if he were to find his tinder, it would only be by daylight. Another course had to be devised. The carbine, as has been already said, could be used only as a club; but this is erroneous —it could be converted into a lance.

Acting upon this impulse Aluna had only to fasten his knife in the Mexican fashion to the tip of his gun. This was readily accomplished, for every hunter out on the plains invariably carries with him a strap arrangement by means of which, should he decide to pass the night under a tree, he either swings himself from a branch, or attaches himself to the trunk of a tree. Tying his knife to the tip of his gun, his equipment was ready. He then returned and leaned up against the stone in such a way that, during the move he was about to make, the bulwark on which he relied for protection could not be moved. From the pressure directed against the stone Aluna was aware that he was dealing with no paltry enemy. Seizing an opportune moment when the jaguar was hurling himself against the obstacle that he was attempting to break down on his side, Aluna thrust out his carbine as a soldier charges, bayonet in hand.

From the jaguar came a loud roar. Something cracked; the carbine, wrested from the hand of its owner, rolled two paces away, while the animal jumped back with a yell. Aluna picked up his gun and examined it. The knife was found to have broken about two-thirds up the blade; of the handle there remained only a fragment measuring one and one-half inches, the rest being in the wound he had made.

This was what caused the howling; this was what caused

the jaguar to run. By now Aluna was desperately in need of a respite; this accordingly afforded him a moment's rest, for he was almost at the end of his strength.

He seized this opportunity to rid himself first of all of the two young jaguars who had been scratching him with their claws while he was engaged in the fight with their father and mother. Grabbing each of them in turn by their hind paws, he dashed their brains out against the walls of the cave. Then, being very thirsty and having no water, he drank the blood of the two little ones.

What especially frightened Aluna was the fact that he was beginning to feel the lack of sleep. Moreover, he was convinced that within a certain length of time this need would become imperative, & could not be ignored. While asleep the jaguar, although momentarily frightened off, might return, push back the stone, or tear one away at one side, & in either event fall unexpectedly on the sleeper and devour him.

To leave was out of the question; the beast might be hiding close by & leap out unexpectedly on the fugitive. So he concluded to sleep where he was, in other words, leaning up against the stone that barred the entrance to the cave, so that the least pressure exerted against the stone would cause him to awake. The stone did not move, and Aluna slept quite tranquilly until on toward two o'clock in the morning.

At two he opened his eyes, conscious of a noise coming from another section of the cave where he believed he recalled having seen a crevice. Indeed, a persistent scratching sound was heard, & small stones falling down like showers of hail indicated that here someone was working from outside. Unluckily all this going on up near the roof, some twelve feet overhead at a height where Aluna was powerless to offer resistance.

He glanced down at his carbine. Useless for firing, useless as a lance, this might be used as a club. Only under such conditions it would be necessary to employ merely the barrel to avoid breaking the butt-end needlessly and thus entirely ruining his gun. Rapidly detaching the knife from the end of the barrel, with what remained of the blade he unscrewed the wood & the locks, arming himself only with the heavy barrel. Then with tense eye, throbbing heart, & arm raised he waited.

But it was soon evident that he would not have long to wait. Heavy stones fell constantly. Through the interstices of the ceiling the breathing of the animal was heard. Soon daylight, or rather night, was visible, a night lighted by a moon that sent vertical rays down through the hole the jaguar was piercing.

Now and again this hole, through which Aluna caught glimpses of the sky aglow with stars, appeared to be hermetically sealed; the animal to test its size from time to time thrust his head down. At such times the rays of light were intercepted, and as a substitute for this ray of light there shone, like two glowing carbuncles, the jaguar's flaming eyes.

Gradually the size of the hole increased. Having lowered his head the beast then pushed in his shoulders; finally head, shoulders and body passed through and the animal coming in from outside dropped silently down on his four paws directly opposite Aluna. Fortunately the blade of the knife that had been plunged in his shoulder prevented him from pouncing immediately on Aluna's throat. He paused an instant, perhaps in pain; this instant was enough for his adversary. The barrel of the carbine now fell on the jaguar's head, stunning him.

Aluna lost no time falling on the beast and with the remaining tip of the knife soon cut the vein in his neck. From this wound ebbed his lifeblood. This act occurred just in time. Aluna was by now worn out by fatigue. Dragging the animal to a lighted spot in the cave where the soil appeared to be formed of soft sand and making a pillow of the beast who was not yet cold, he fell into a profound sleep from which he did not awake until long after daybreak.

XV : ALONG THE SACRAMENTO

Now THIS mode of life which because of its freedom has so much charm, especially for men born & raised in the country who frequently devote their entire lives to it, had for us, too, an inexpressible lure. Tiring as it was to travel semi-weekly to San Francisco to sell the products of our hunting, we did not take this into consideration, or rather we accepted it, being, especially in the beginning, well remunerated for the concomitant fatigue. Our profits frequently ran as high as three or four hundred piasters a week. The first month we took in, after all expenses were paid, 400 piasters; however, during the last two & particularly during the last week when we cleared only 150 piasters, the drop proved that this speculation was about over.

Hunting for one thing had begun to thin out in this region; furthermore, the game we were after withdrew toward Lake Laguna, the country of the Kinklas Indians, searching for regions where they would be less pursued. Finally plans were formulated to push further away toward the northeast and find a market for what game we brought in at Sacramento City. Upon our arrival we secured full information as to whether the placers of the Sacramento surpassed those of the San Joaquín, & whether the Young, the Yuba, or the Feather River was preferable to the mining-camps at Sonora, Pine Pass, and Murphy's. So when our game had largely disappeared, this plan was put into execution &, leaving our boat at Sonoma, we traveled on toward the American fork. From there the range of Californian mountains was crossed from west to east. After one and one-half days hunting our poor horse was loaded down with game. We now found ourselves on the banks of the Sacramento. After ascending the river for two or three hours a boat of salmon fishermen came up &, for the sum of four piasters, agreed to ferry us & our game over to the opposite bank. Although the river at this point must have been nearly a quarter of a mile broad, yet our horse was able to swim across.

From the fishermen information was secured as to conditions at the mines. While they could not give us much definite news, nevertheless they had heard rumors to the effect that the Americans were ruining everything by their banditry. This did not in the least astonish Tillier and me, having already had a sample of their conduct along the San Joaquín River. Aluna for his part merely shrugged his shoulders and screwed up his lips, as much as to say, 'Ah, my word, I have

certainly seen enough of them!' Aluna cordially disliked all
Americans, whom he believed capable of any kind of crime.
He invariably had a fund of stories to relate about them
where such acts as being stabbed by a knife, or shot with a
pistol, were not penalized by juries who were both stupid
and indiscreet.

We pushed on to Sacramento City and even as far as Sutter's Fort to ascertain for ourselves how far we might rely
on these rumors. What the salmon-fishers had said was confirmed; the mines were in the throes of a revolution. Fearing
to lose what little wealth we had so laboriously collected, we
now retraced our steps, descending the Sacramento on a boat
that we rented for forty piasters.

At Sacramento City, our game sold for eighty dollars; near
the American fork, the dollar passes for legal tender, whereas
on the Sacramento all transactions are computed in piasters.
The rented boat belonged to the salmon-fishers, who had
guaranteed to land us where we chose provided, however,
that not more than four days were required to go down from
Sacramento City to Benicia, below Suisun Bay. Aluna followed along the left bank with the horse.

So magnificent is the Sacramento Valley that it belies description, bounded as it is on the east by the Sierra Nevada,
on the west by the California mountains, and on the north
by Mt. Shasta. From north to south it measures approximately 200 miles.

When the snows melt and the Sacramento overflows the
level rises eight or nine feet. This can be readily recognized
by the traces of sediment deposited on the trunks of trees.
This slime, like that of the Nile, remaining on the banks of

the Sacramento is what gives fresh life to the soil. The trees lining the banks are primarily oaks, willows, laurels, & pines. On both banks, near the river, were visible herds of cattle, deer, and even wild horses.

In certain places the Sacramento is one-half mile wide; the average depth is three or four meters, the result being that ships of 200 tons can navigate. In the Sacramento are found great quantities of salmon which are also numerous throughout its affluents. The salmon leave the sea in spring & ascend the river in swarms for about 500 miles. By following the main stream no obstacles are encountered, but on beyond, whether following the Sacramento or venturing up its affluents, their ascent is impeded by cascades, by dams made by the Indians or erected by farmers for some definite purpose, or even by gold-seekers, exploiting the rivers.

Here the fish struggle in vain to cross these bars or barricades. When approaching the limb of a tree or a rock which might retard their progress, they approach, swim along it, dart underneath, trace an arc, then mustering every ounce of strength, jump frequently twelve or fifteen feet up in the air. Their leap is always so gauged that they will fall into the upper waters toward which they are moving.

At the fork of the Sacramento and the San Joaquín lie a dozen low, wooded islands characterized by impassable marshy areas. These are covered with tule, a growth indigenous to all low and humid regions in this country. To devotees of waterfowl this is a veritable collector's paradise, for these lagoons swarm with duck, cormorant, stork, kingfishers, and magpies of every kind & description. In four days we were in Benicia. After settling our bill with the fishermen we pushed on, hunting as we traveled across the prairie to the ranch of Sonoma, where we had left our boat. That same evening after an absence of six weeks we reached San Francisco.

Here Gauthier and Mirandole were found to be still quite ill, figuratively speaking, from the last fire. They had lost approximately as much merely by moving their goods as others had actually lost by the fire.

The morning of our arrival we happened to run across one of our friends, Adolphe by name, who lived on a ranch between San Francisco Bay and the Californian range. Adolphe invited us to come & spend a day or so at his ranch, promising to allow us to participate in a lively bear-hunt, which was to take place within the next day or two. We accepted. During these two days Tillier and I hoped to find time to discuss what plans we would adopt for the future.

XVI : HUNTING BEAR

THE HUNT that had been promised by our friend Adolphe was set for the day following the arrival of Tillier, Aluna, and myself at his country place which was located, as I have said, between the San Francisco Bay and the Californian mountains.

The bear which was to be pursued was the gray bear, *Ursus horribilis*. For several days now he had been coming down off the pine-clad mountains and, no longer satisfied with dining off the small reeds that fringe the course of the brooks, of which these animals are inordinately fond, had begun to steal cattle, thus inflicting heavy losses on the owners of the ranchos. Because of this the rancheros had united against the common enemy, and since they were all Mexicans a decision had been reached that the animal was to be captured by means of the lasso.

Aluna, noted for his long years of experience in this very type of hunting, had been placed in charge of the expedition. Thirty men remained in ambush, men and horses standing ready to render mutual assistance. At dawn the bear descended, the hunters had the wind against them & a bear of less size and milder nature would have recoiled before this hint of danger. The animal in question stopped, reared up on his hind legs, caught the wind and, recognizing clearly that trouble was brewing, concluded to go directly over to the first clump of trees where the leader of the bear-hunt was hiding.

This leader was our old friend Aluna who, accepting the challenge, bravely left his shelter & marched directly toward him. When within thirty feet of the bear he hurled his lasso toward him; this fell around his neck & one of his paws. Then, knotting the end of the lasso to the pommel of his saddle, he called out to companions, 'Come on now, we have him!'

The bear remained for a moment stunned at the brusqueness of the attack of which he failed to sense the full significance. He had received a blow without experiencing any pain and seemed to regard with astonishment, although no uneasiness, the first rope around him.

Three or four lassos were now hurled simultaneously from different directions. All reached the animal & held him more or less securely. The bear at this point turned to charge but the riders to a man urged their horses to a gallop and rode at top speed in advance. Enmeshed in these ropes the bear experienced considerable difficulty in following them. The remaining hunters coming out, in turn, from their hiding places entangled him still further. In an instant the bear, with thirty lassos around him, seemed to be held as if in a net.

He was now powerless to fight against such odds and for the first time began no doubt to regret having come down from his mountain lair, to which he yearned to return. But this could not be accomplished without the consent of the hunters. For an instant he attempted to break away; once he seemed about to succeed.

In a short time the thirty riders and the thirty horses were dragged 500 feet and forced, because of his great strength, to follow in his wake. Then all veered simultaneously and, with cries of encouragement mingled with the clashing of spurs, succeeded in gaining the upper hand.

The power of resistance exhibited by this great brute was frightful to witness. At times when the slightest opportunity offered he was able against our full force to drag us after him. His eyes resembled two fountains of dripping blood; his mouth seemed to belch forth flames like those of a chimera; his groans resounded a league away.

Finally, not after a hunt but after a fight lasting an hour, the animal yielded; he now let himself be dragged along as far as Don Castro's rancho where, utterly exhausted, he was killed with rifles. He weighed 1100 pounds, double that of an ordinary steer. He was divided among all three hunters. Some of this bear-meat sold in the San Francisco market for one piaster a pound for which the butchers, however, paid three francs.

This hunt recalled to Aluna's mind the happy days of his youth and gave him the idea, which he confided to us, of going out to hunt bear along the Mariposa and of not returning to San Francisco until on toward the middle of September. His proposal was accepted and the very evening of our return to the city preparations were made to depart.

XVII : THE MARIPOSA

AT THIS TIME different arrangements had to be made. What was lacking was not a boat but a wagon and a second horse. By selling our boat for approximately the same price we had paid for it we were able to secure both.

The presidios and ranchos which we ourselves dubbed 'presides' & 'ranchs' have already been mentioned. Presidios, as has been said, are small forts at which a few soldiers are stationed. Ranchos are a kind of farm. The name of *rancheria* is applied when a few houses are grouped together forming a small village. Missions & pueblos now require explanation.

The missions were originally large establishments maintained for the benefit of Indian subjects desiring to be instructed in the Christian faith who, once instructed in the faith, were expected to devote themselves to some specific work. Whoever has seen one mission has seen them all; they consist generally of a building built around a large central court and contain a number of cells pierced with windows & doors. At the corner of the edifice usually towers a church with a belfry. Trees and a gushing fountain bring a note of freshness into the court.

These missions were Capuchin missions.* Each of them was in charge of two Fathers, one to instruct the neophytes along educational lines, the other to direct manual labor. In the interior of the establishment were forges, mills, tanneries, soap-factories, joiners works, and carpenter shops. All this was so distributed as to leave in the principal wing rooms for monks & visitors and in the other end of the building school rooms, supply houses, and infirmaries.

Around the establishment extended gardens and beyond the gardens clustered Indian huts, usually built of straw and reeds. The Indian neophytes were fed at the mission. Although the Capuchins were not remarkable cooks, yet since there was no way to rectify this out in this remote land, they prepared their own food as well as that of the Indians. This food consisted of corn cakes, of boiled beef or mutton, and of all kinds of fruits. They did not drink wine. What wine was made in the mission or brought in from the settlements was kept for invalids or reserved for visitors. Neophytes & workers were instructed gratuitously. Everything in these establishments was accomplished by persuasion, not by force.

Pueblos are nothing more than villages that were established originally by soldiers who had seen service at the presidios and to whom had been granted, in exchange for these services, a definite amount of land, which they were free to

*All missions in Upper California were under the Franciscan Order.

select wherever they preferred, provided the land they desired was vacant.* Each man exploited this land in his own fashion. California as a whole contained only four pueblos: Nuestra Señora de Los Ángeles, Santa Bárbara, Branciforte, and San José.

The day of our departure we went down to pass the night at the pueblo of San José, situated in the center of a magnificent valley on the Guadalupe River, a small stream that descends from the Californian mountains and finally empties into the lower end of San Francisco Bay. This is some four leagues from Mission Santa Clara with which it is connected by a long avenue entirely shaded by live oaks. These oaks were originally planted by the Fathers with the idea that once they were grown they would cast their protecting shade over the faithful who went from the pueblo of San José to hear mass at Mission Santa Clara.†

The pueblo of San José was built in 1777, or 1778.‡ In 1848, that is before gold was discovered, its population numbered about 600 inhabitants who occupied 100 or 150 brick houses, scattered on both sides of a road lined with great trees.§ At the present, or rather at the time when we stopped overnight at the pueblo, the settlement consisted of 1,000 houses two or three stories high, while the population, which then totaled five thousand was rapidly increasing. The result was that instead of giving away free land, as had been done before, the

*These pueblos were actually colonized by settlers brought up for this purpose from Mexico. Many, however, were soldiers.
†These oaks were indigenous to California; along this road the Fathers planted the Australian eucalyptus.
‡San José de Guadalupe was founded on November 29, 1777.
§All early houses were built of adobe, or blocks of sun-baked clay.

tendency on the contrary was to sell it at a good price. In October, 1849, there had been a movement to make the pueblo of San José the capital of California, and this proposal, sponsored by the Californian convention, had tended materially to increase the number of inhabitants & to inflate the value of land. With this expectation there had just been completed on the main square at the time of our arrival a building to house the legislature. As a result the pueblo of San José, being connected with Santa Clara Bay by the Guadalupe River and being situated between San Francisco and Monterey, was the second city in the land.

The pueblo of San José has its mission, founded in 1797, which is situated fifteen miles north at the foot of a small chain of mountains called the Bolbones, which are nothing more than isolated spurs of the major Californian mountains. During the few hours we remained at the pueblo of San José we secured some information and ascertained to our satisfaction that we might sell our game here as advantageously as at San Francisco.

In the morning we departed and went directly on toward the Californian mountains. We had not traveled more than a day when Aluna detected the presence of bear by two infallible signs: first, by their tracks left on the sandy ground; then by the way in which the reeds, of which they are extremely fond and which grow on the banks of small streams, had been cut. We pitched camp and waited for night to fall. This was to be our apprenticeship in this new kind of hunt, into which Aluna initiated us during the night. All three of us stood close together; Aluna held his lasso and carbine; Tillier and I had our double-barreled guns equipped with bayonets.

Aluna took the precaution of leaning against a young oak as thick as his thigh. Thus we waited.

Two hours later a bear descended from the mountain and passed twenty paces away from us. He was a black bear of small stature and did not weigh over 250 or 300 pounds. Aluna threw his lasso which wrapped around him three or four times, then quickly tied the opposite end to the tree, took his carbine, ran toward the bear &, while the creature was struggling in this strange trap, killed him with a ball through the ear. This was a peculiar way of hunting bear that was characteristic of Aluna, but a way which, owing to our ignorance of how to handle a lasso, we could not employ. Aluna having shown us how he captured him, then demonstrated how we were to make captures.

Our rôle was even more simple. After our bear was killed, cleaned, and kept safely away from jackals by being hung from a limb, we then followed the track of a wolf and, exercising care to have the wind in our favor, searched for another post. This was not difficult to find. Aluna, stopping us at a point that seemed propitious, placed his lasso and his carbine in our hands & took my double-barreled gun. He then stood by to show me how I was to make my capture.

After waiting an hour down came a bear. The brute stopped to drink not more than thirty paces away. Aluna aimed at him saying, 'With the way this bear is acting, I could kill him with a single shot; however, I shall merely wound him as you will see, to demonstrate what you should do.' After this remark the attack started. The bear, struck in the shoulder, gave a roar, looking around to see from where this injury had come. Aluna now appeared and walked toward him.

The bear, seeing his adversary advance rather than retreat, took several steps forward to meet him and, having arrived five or six paces from Aluna, reared up on his hind legs, preparatory to smothering him. Aluna seized this opportunity, aimed at his breast, and fired at close range. The bear rolled over in a heap. 'This is how it is done,' Aluna called to us. 'If by chance you are forced to fire twice, or your gun sticks, you have your bayonet left. At the first opportunity, I will show you how to use it, but this is enough for tonight. Moreover, by now these bears must recognize the sound of guns; they have heard three of them, and will not come again.'

The following day our two bear were transported to the pueblo of San José and sold for 100 piasters each.

The following night we had our first real experience. Luck was with me; the bear came within fifteen paces of us. Tillier and I held ourselves in readiness to assist one another. The bear stopped and, finding a clump of reeds that he relished, reared up on his hind legs, and with his front paws clutched the clump of reeds much as a reaper gathers a sheaf of wheat. Then he began to eat, bending his head down to find the most tender stalks. In this position his chest was exposed. I fired. The ball entered just below the shoulder. The bear staggered and rolled into the brook. Struggling desperately to rise, he was unable to climb up either one of the two steep ascents along the bank. At the end of five minutes the death agonies began and he died uttering growls that, if tradition is to be believed, would have caused all the bears in the Californian mountains to congregate.

This terminated our apprenticeship. We were now fullfledged hunters. In the daytime when we were not too tired,

we indulged in the usual type of hunt. During such expeditions we brought down squirrel, hare, & partridge. Deer were
far rarer than in the vicinity of Sonoma; we killed only one.

On the same jaunt on which I took my deer I killed a magnificent white-and-blue snake. Lying curled up in a clump of
lupins, with his mouth open among the exquisite blue flowers
that capped the bushes, he had apparently lured a gray squirrel that, fascinated by his magnetic eye, descended noisily from
branch to branch. I sent a ball through the head of the enormous reptile that hissed as he writhed. The spell broken, the
squirrel bounded instantly from the middle to the upper
branches and from this tree over to a neighboring tree. As
for the serpent, not knowing whether or not he was poisonous
I was careful enough to remain at a distance, but he was much
too engrossed to pay any attention to me. My shot had carried off all the upper part of his head just behind the eyes.
Aluna recognized him as belonging to the boa family, that
is, to non-poisonous reptiles. He was over nine feet long.

The destruction of this reptile & a meeting with the Tachi
Indians who had laid plans to carry off our wagon and our
two horses were the only extraordinary episodes that occurred
during the month passed in the Californian mountains. Aluna
strangled one of these Indians with his lasso; another was
wounded by a shot from our gun. The Indians, on the other
hand, killed one of our horses with an arrow. Fortunately this
was the horse we had just bought, and not Aluna's animal.

The Indians' arrows are of reeds, tipped with feathers, and
measure about a yard in length, six inches from their tip a
smaller reed is inserted into the upper part; the result being
that, when an attempt is made to extricate an arrow from

the body of man or beast, this secondary section remains in the wound and only the upper end comes out. Instances are quite rare when the presence of this foreign body, which can seldom be removed from the wound, does not cause death. The tips of the arrows are equipped with bits of sharp glass that cut. I secured five or six of these arrows which were picked up on the battle-ground. They had been aimed toward us but not one had touched us.

Toward the end of the month, the same situation developed that had occurred beyond San Francisco, that is, the country had either been stripped of all game, or the game had gone up or rather gone down toward the Tulare Valley; in other words, to a region too remote from San Francisco or even from the pueblo at San José for meat to arrive fresh. And so our means of livelihood had failed us again and we were obliged to return to San Francisco. However, I had nearly attained my cherished goal.

XVIII : LIFE AS A WAITER

MY GOAL was to open up a small business of some kind in San Francisco. The status of the gold-seeker would be lucrative if it could be carried on by companies, but our roving and capricious natures render difficult any kind of coöperation. Twenty or thirty may leave in a body, promise to remain together and devise the most elaborate plans. But once at the placers each man forms his own opinion, holds stubbornly to it, goes off by himself, and the group disbands, frequently even before operations have been begun. The result of all this is that, as in all human ventures, out of fifty miners who go to the placers, only five or six who are persevering by nature make fortunes; the others, less stable, become discouraged, change locations, or return to San Francisco. Death, too, claims its toll.

[148]

Upon leaving for the mines—& I have every right to give this advice to those who come after me, not having followed for my own part what I shall now advise—it is necessary to provide supplies, ammunition, and tools for the entire time to be spent there; to select some place and remain there permanently from the time this claim shows a yield; to construct a good shelter, & so avoid being affected by the damp night and the cold mornings; to avoid working in the water during the heat of the sun, that is from eleven o'clock in the morning until three o'clock in the afternoon; and, finally, to be moderate with strong drink and to live on a regular schedule. Whoever fails to follow these instructions will either accomplish nothing and so grow discouraged, or will fall ill and in all probability die.

There is still another thing of which I am fully convinced, namely that in addition to searching for gold there are ten, twenty, or even one hundred ways to make a fortune in San Francisco, for while the former method which at first glance appears fairly simple and easy yet is, on the contrary, one of the least reliable.

While in San Francisco I had occasion to observe that unquestionably the best speculation to make, among the small ventures that came to my attention, was to purchase wine in job lots from the ships that arrived and to sell this wine at retail. Not knowing this business, however, I had to learn it. As I have said, having once landed in San Francisco, the past is utterly ignored, and any social position held in the old world vanishes like so much mist, or, if it continues to adhere, merely tends to befog future prospects.

When I returned to San Francisco the first person I met

on the docks was the son of a French nobleman, who had become a boatman. So I felt that I, whom the revolution of 1830 had deprived of hereditary rights, could stoop to accepting a position as waiter in one of the hotels. Tillier found, in a place that had handled our products, a position as butcher-boy at one hundred piasters a month; I, with the aid of my friend, Gauthier, who boarded at Hotel Richelieu, secured a place in the hotel as inspector, at a monthly wage of 125 piasters. Table d'hôte was served for two piasters, each patron being allowed one-half bottle of wine. This was twice the amount served in Paris; but as a matter of fact it was just about half as good. I remained a month at Hotel Richelieu; during this time I received a liberal education in wines, alcoholic drinks, and liquors.

My education completed, since I had now saved up as my share while associated with Aluna, Tillier and Leon, something like 1000 piasters, which was sufficient to open a small business, I left Hotel Richelieu and started out to find a small office. I found just what I was looking for at the corner of Pacific Street—a wooden shack, suitable for a wine-shop on the lower floor which, in addition to the one room, had an office for bookkeeping, and two sleeping chambers.

I rented these insignificant quarters for 400 piasters a month & at once began work. Obviously with a capital of only 1000 piasters and with a monthly rental of 400 piasters no time must be lost to prevent rent from eating up capital. As I had anticipated, this proved to be an excellent speculation; the Americans ate and drank from morning until night, quitting work from time to time to have a little drink or a bite to eat. Then came night—the best time of all—for the police force, although less experienced, was more intelligent than the French police in that they permitted wine-merchants and cafés to remain open all night long, a system that kept the city in a healthy condition by making it as lively by night as by day. This tended to eliminate robberies or assassinations, for every fifty paces there was an open door and a lighted house. However, assassinations still occurred, but largely in brawls, or from motives of revenge.

The gay gamblers' places were what turned night into day. Now I was quite near La Polka and not far from El Dorado. Among our patrons, as a result, were both ruined & successful gamblers, two contrasting types, the type that weeps and the type that laughs.

What an opportunity to study the philosophy of daily life! Men, arriving direct from the mines, would often lose 50,000 francs in gold-nuggets in a single evening, being then forced to turn their pockets inside out looking for enough gold-dust to buy a small drink. If the dust was not there, they would beg a glass on credit, promising to pay on the next trip in from the mines. Life inside of these gambling houses was hideous, the stakes were for gold bullion & when the gambler had won, his stake was weighed in the scales. Even necklaces, chains, watches were staked; their valuation was fixed at random and accepted at such valuation.

One night, upon hearing the cry 'Murder!' we rushed out to find a Frenchman being assassinated by three Mexicans. He had just been stabbed by knives in three places and his life was slowly ebbing from these three mortal wounds. We carried him in this dying condition into the house, but he expired before this was reached. His name was Lacour. Of his three assassins, only one was captured and condemned to be hung. Inasmuch as this was only the second or third execution that had taken place the result was that everyone still enjoyed witnessing such spectacles.

Unfortunately, since the scaffolding needed to support the gallows, gallows that were to remain permanently in order to frighten assassins, had not yet been erected by carpenters, an artesian well, quite the reverse of gallows, was being dug, the idea being to lower the culprit into a hole in place of hoisting him up on the gallows. But these were needed to supply water to the cisterns in the city; moreover, as has already been said, there was an acute shortage of water in San Francisco.

Lacking the European type of gibbet, the maritime type of gallows had to be used. An American frigate offered to lend one of its yard-arms, an offer that had been gratefully accepted in San Francisco by the judicial authorities, since in place of a United States citizen being the victim, the culprit was a Mexican. The execution was scheduled, so that all might enjoy it at their leisure, to take place at eleven o'clock in the morning. By eight o'clock, Pacific Street, where the prison was located, was thronged with crowds.

At half-past ten appeared the policemen, readily recognizable by the white batons hanging from their button-holes by way of decoration. They immediately entered the prison, whose door closed after them, taking to the condemned, through this brief opening, murmurs of impatience from twenty thousand spectators. Finally the door reopened and the long anticipated victim appeared. His hands were empty and his head bare; he wore split trousers, a short Mexican vest, and carried his poncho thrown over one shoulder.

The culprit was now taken down to the main wharf where a boat was lying in wait; into this he climbed with the policemen and executioners. Twenty-five or thirty boats pushed off simultaneously from the docks, loaded with curious spectators who were unwilling to miss any part of the performance. All along the main wharf and the entire beach crowds thronged. I was among those who remained ashore, lacking courage to see more.

Having reached the frigate, the condemned man walked courageously aboard and there made final preparations to be hung, even aiding the executioner to place the rope around his neck, adjusting it in a satisfactory manner around his throat. This completed, over his head was thrown a great black veil that hid his face from the crowds. At a given sig- four sailors pulled the rope jerking their victim off his feet, raising him to the end of the main yard-sail. For an instant the body writhed convulsively, but was soon motionless. The execution was now over. The body was left exposed for part of the day to the public gaze, then at evening it was lowered, placed in a boat, & removed to the cemetery at the presidio.

XIX : DEMON FIRE AGAIN

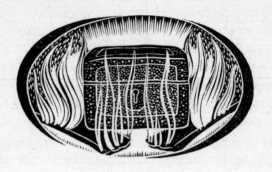

DUE TO the shortage of water, an elaborate fire organization existed in San Francisco. In the main square a fine artesian well was being dug which was designed to supply water to all cisterns in the city. In anticipation of this water supply the firemen held daily practice without water; they could be seen running with their pumps, their American helmets, & their blue trousers from one end of the city to the other, which invariably gave rise to the belief that fire had broken out in San Francisco.

During my relatively improvident youth, I was of the belief that the lack of a safe place in which to lock up my money was the sole cause of my prodigality. Not knowing where to deposit it safely, I allowed it freely to slip into the pockets

of others; so my first precaution, when I had my own establishment, was to procure a strong-box.

I found a splendid one built of iron that was so heavy that
I could scarcely move it. I was asked 150 piasters for it, but
I finally secured it for 100 piasters—which was, I believe, a
good bargain. I was convinced that in case of fire a solid iron
chest would be a melting-pot where I should find my gold
and silver melted into bullion, but where I could ultimately
recover it. So I placed my chest at the foot of my counter
and every night stored away my profits for the day.

These profits were quite satisfactory for after all expenses
were paid they averaged 100 & frequently 150 francs. I had
been able out of these profits to purchase at quite a favorable
price five or six lots of wine and several casks of liquors and
brandy from the captain of the *Mazagran*, a ship in the harbor,
and still had something like 4000 or 5000 francs in my chest
when suddenly, on the morning of September fifteenth, I was
awakened by my two servants who pounded on my door
crying 'Fire!'

This, as I have said, was a terrible cry, this cry of fire in
San Francisco, which was built entirely of wood, especially
when the city streets, in place of being left in their natural
condition of dust, or mire were paved with wood and tended
to spread fires by encouraging them. Upon hearing this cry
of fire, the one thought is how to escape death. Despite this
axiom of incontestible truth, I ran first for my trunk, turned
the key, and threw it out of the window; I then put on my
trousers, and started to escape down the stairs.

But it was now too late; there remained open only the
route used by my trunk. I had no time to delay, so I seized

this opportunity and jumped out through the window. The fire had started in the cellar of the adjoining house which was unoccupied. Once the flames reached my cellar, full of wines and alcohols, it would be nothing but a huge furnace which the combined efforts of all the firemen in San Francisco would be powerless to check. As for the chest, there was no hope of saving it, my one desire was to save what it contained.

The fire lasted two and one-half hours, burning 300 houses and all the bakery quarters. By good luck my baker lived above Pacific Avenue; the fire did not reach him. He offered me a refuge which I accepted. This good man had the reputation of being a fair and just man; he was called Aristide. There remained one last hope—my chest. I waited in agony until the ashes were cold enough so that I might begin a search in which my friends Tillier, Mirandole, Gauthier, and my two boys joined. One of us constantly guarded the ashes, so that no one would come in and do what we expected to do. Finally after three days it was possible to begin to handle the ashes with a pick-axe.

I knew where the chest had been in the main room and so consequently knew where it ought to be in the cellar, since its weight led me to believe that it had fallen directly down. But however much we dug, excavated, and explored, we did not find a trace of the chest. I was convinced that my poor chest had been stolen. Suddenly I found a kind of iron stalactite, scarcely as large as an egg, full of rough knobs and shimmering with the most beautiful tints of gold and silver. My chest had melted like wax before a hot fire, & this was all that remained of my strong-box! Again the brass of Corinth had been found!

I could not believe my eyes when I saw that of a mass representing two cubic feet of surface, there remained a residue not larger than an egg! I give you my word I could not understand how the solitary unique souvenir of a chest weighing sixty pounds, could be merely a gilded iron stalactite weighing only five or six ounces. Such a thing seemed incredible. Although an Englishman offered me 100 piasters for this bit of iron, which he wished to present to the Bureau of Mineralogy at London, I declined his offer.

Even so I desperately needed those 100 piasters. Except for what was in my trunk, I had lost everything. Fortunately, in my trunk were secreted a few gold nuggets I had collected during our expeditions to the placers and which I was saving to take back to France as gifts. These nuggets I immediately converted into gold and silver coin. By selling whatever was not strictly necessary, I scraped together 300 or 400 piasters. This was enough to refinance some kind of a business; but I was weary of coping with bad luck. An unkind fate seemed to have conspired to prevent me from passing a certain level. Had I lost all my resources in France, I might have tried again & had I had enough determination I might have won out against misfortune.

But back in France I had left my family & some additional resources. So I decided to give up my place to some of the numerous competitors who daily thronged hopefully to these gates, and since Captain Andy, master of the *Mazagran*, needed an officer, I arranged to serve under him on his ship on the return trip from San Francisco to Bordeaux, Brest, or Havre.

The deal was soon completed, my terms being easy. What

I wished above all else was to return to France without diminishing by the expense of passage what little remained. The departure was fixed for early in October, but was postponed until the eighteenth. After September twenty-fourth, I was at work on the ship; my duties consisted in taking on ballast of stones.

On Sunday, October seventeenth, I went ashore for the last time. Here several Frenchmen were expecting me at Hotel Richelieu for a farewell dinner. Whether this was sadder or gayer than that at Havre would be difficult to say. At Havre we were buoyant with hope; at San Francisco we were saddened by disappointment.

The following day, October eighteenth, we weighed anchor and that same evening under an excellent east wind that carried us along at eight or nine knots an hour, land dropped out of sight.

XX : CONCLUSION

AND WHAT shall I say of this land that I was leaving almost as eagerly as I had once entered? I shall tell the truth. In so far as California has been known primarily for her remarkable climate, the fertility of her soil, the richness of her vegetation, the navigability of her rivers, California has been virtually unknown or rather erroneously known. After the capture of San Juan de Ulloa, Mexico offered it to France who declined the offer. After the capture of its capital it was transferred for $15,000,000 to the Americans, who purchased it merely to prevent it from passing over into the hands of England. For a time California under this control remained as she was, that is, a region neglected by the entire world except for a few tenacious missionaries, some nomadic Indians, and a handful of venturesome emigrants.

How this resounding cry, the far-reaching cry of 'Gold!'

reached the entire world is well known. At the start the news was heard with the callousness of mistrust. The Americans who laboriously till new soil and clear new lands had already recognized the inherent richness of the country, that is, the fertility of the soil. Whoever had sown & reaped even one harvest had been able to see the ratio between what he planted and what he harvested; and was certain to reap a fortune. Why raise his head above the plow at the cry 'Gold!'

Then finally some particles of this gold were exhibited, gold that had come from the American fork. But Captain Folsom, to whom these were shown, merely shrugged his shoulders saying 'That's mica!' In the meantime, two or three messengers, accompanied by a dozen Indians, came in from Sutter's Fort. They had come for implements suitable for washing sands. With their pockets bulging with gold-dust they told marvellous tales of this discovery which was changing the Sacramento into a second Pactolus.

A few citizens now followed them back, intending to enter the employ of Mr. Sutter who was calling for workers. But eight days later they were back again, searching for equipment for themselves & giving out reports about these mines that were even more fabulous than those of the first-comers. What resembled a kind of fever then seized the inhabitants of the settlements, the workmen at the ports, the sailors on board ship.

Here is what, on July twenty-ninth, was written by Mr. Colton, alcalde of Sonoma. 'The mining-fever has completely disrupted everything here, as it has everywhere; laborers & harvesters can no longer be found; all the men in town have left for the Sierra Nevada. Spades, pick-axes, sauce-pans, earthen porringers, bottles, phials, snuff-boxes, hoes, barrels & even the stills have all been requisitioned & have left the village with them.'* Simultaneously Mr. Larkin, the American consul, observed that the exodus was reaching such proportions that he felt impelled to make Mr. Buchanan, Secretary of State, a report in which occurs this passage: 'All the landlords, lawyers, store-keepers, mechanics, and laborers have started for the mines with their families; workmen earning from five to eight dollars a day have left the city. The local newspaper has ceased to appear, lacking editors. A large number of volunteers from the New York regiment have deserted. A government vessel from the Sandwich Islands, actually at anchor, has lost its entire crew. If this situation continues, the capital and all the other cities will be depopulated; whaling-vessels coming into the bay will be deserted by their crews. What steps shall Colonel Mason take to retain his men? This is a problem I cannot solve.'†

Then, eight days later, Colonel Mason wrote in turn: 'For several days now the situation has been so acute that I have expected the garrison at Monterey to desert in a body. The temptation, I must admit, is great; there is little danger of being captured & there is every expectation of an enormous compensation, double in one day what a soldier receives monthly in board & salary. To keep a servant is impossible; a workman, no matter what his profession, will not work for

*Walter Colton was alcalde at Monterey, not Sonoma. He subsequently joined the gold-rush.

†Prior to Colton's report, Thomas O. Larkin had sent in an official report dated June 1, 1848, to Washington. The substance of this report appears in this quotation. This report was published with the President's annual message of December 5, 1848, in *House Executive Documents*, 30 Congress, 2 Session, Washington, 1848-1849.

less than eighty francs a day and often demands as much as
100 or 110 francs. What is to be done under such conditions?
The prices of ordinary commodities are moreover so high
and domestic labor so costly that only those who earn 500 or
600 francs daily can afford a servant.'*

On the other hand, here is what our consul at Monterey,
Mr. Moerenhaut, reports: 'Never in any country in the world
has there been, I believe, such an upheaval. The women and
children are constantly being left alone on the most isolated
farms, for even the Indians are taken away by their masters,
or have left of their own accord to hunt gold; this emigration
keeps increasing and is constantly gaining momentum. The
roads are thronged with men, horses, and wagons; but the
cities and villages are deserted.'†

If you would like to have some idea of this exodus, follow
the route of a lone brig that is bound for San Francisco, in
command of a Peruvian, Captain Munraz. He is coming up
from Arica, having received his orders from San Francisco
before gold was discovered. He is coming, as is his custom,
to complete his annual exchange of goods, and is ignorant of
changed conditions.

Forced by contrary winds to put in at San Diego, he in-
quired for the latest news from California. Here he was told
what was taking place; how the city, which years ago numbered only about fifteen or twenty houses, now had from
three to four hundred, and upon his arrival at the port he
found a life and an activity equal to what Telemachus encountered upon touching at Salente.

*Colonel R. B. Mason's official letter was published in *House Executive
Documents*, 31 Congress, 1 Session, No. 17, Washington, 1849-1850.
†Mr. Moerenhaut took up his official duties at Monterey on August 3,
1848.

Having heard this good news he departed with high hopes not only, thanks to this growing activity, over selling his cargo, but of securing new commissions and offers. The weather was perfect. Mt. Diablo, with the light striking it, fairly glistened and the brig directed its course direct to the anchorage at Yerba Buena. But one thing seemed incomprehensible to Captain Munraz: he did not see a single ship at sea, nor a man moving along the shores. What then had become of this activity of which he had heard, this growing city that had been making all the countryside resound with the pounding of hammers and the buzzing of saws? From all appearances this was like entering the domains of beauty asleep in the woods, except that even the sleepers were invisible. Perhaps some fête was taking place at the pueblo of San José. Captain Munraz consulted his calendar. Saturday, July eighth, no fête that day!

Captain Munraz continued on ahead. He believed that he must be dreaming. Neither a war, a fire, nor an Indian uprising, however, was causing this silence, this profound solitude. The city was still there; the houses were still intact; on the docks the astounded crew noted rows of tonnage piled high; along the wharves goods of all kinds were piled up at the doors of warehouses.

Captain Munraz now hailed several ships lying at anchor. But these ships were as solitary, as silent as the docks and the warehouses. Suddenly the thought—the only one possible under the circumstances—came to Captain Munraz that the entire population of San Francisco had been recently wiped out by cholera, yellow fever, typhus, or some epidemic. To go on would have been the height of imprudence.

So Captain Munraz gave orders to come about. Then, as he was passing a small Mexican brig, he believed he saw something stirring aboard that resembled a human being. He hailed this phantom. An old Mexican sailor, his head enveloped in bandages, rose up from his knees. 'Ship, ahoy!' called Captain Munraz, 'what has become of the inhabitants of San Francisco?'

'Oh!' replied the old Mexican, 'they have all left for the land of gold!'

'And where is that?' laughingly asked Captain Munraz.

'Along the banks of the Sacramento are mountains and valleys where a man merely has to stoop down and gather up gold. I am a sick man or I would go along to this land with the rest.'

Ten minutes later Captain Munraz's ship was empty. The sailors had gone ashore, started toward the Sacramento, and the poor Captain left alone had to anchor and moor his ship as well as possible near the other empty vessels.

So at the cry of 'Gold!' everyone rushed for the placers in the belief that the only way to make a fortune was to collect gold. And each man worked at the diggings to the best of his ability aided by such tools as he was able to procure and sustained by such resources as he could command, some using pick-axes & others spades, boat-hooks, or even fire-shovels. Some, having no tools, dug down into the soil with their own fingers. This earth was then washed with napkins, plates, sauce-pans, and straw hats.

From all directions swarmed men on horseback, families in wagons, poor devils on foot who had perhaps traveled steadily for 100 miles without a rest. Each one, upon seeing cups already filled with virgin gold, was seized with the fever and immediately jumped off his horse or wagon and started digging in order not to lose a tiny bit of this amazingly rich land, a single second of valuable time.

As a matter of fact, instances of this were not lacking. Mr. Neilly and Mr. Crowly, assisted by six men, had collected in six days 10½ pounds of gold, valued at some 15,000 or 16,000 francs. Mr. Vaca of New Mexico, with the aid of four men, took out 17 pounds of gold in one week. Mr. Morris, aided only by one Indian, had, in a single claim in one ravine found 16,000 francs in gold-dust.

This type of vertigo kept constantly increasing. Whoever left San Francisco left with the deliberate intention of becoming a miner, of searching, digging, and taking out with his own hands this precious metal. Unfortunately, this of all kinds of speculation was the least certain, the most precarious and one that would be quickly exhausted. The vast fortunes of San Francisco were not made at the mines. The mines were merely the aim, the pretext. Providence, casting her eye into the far future, had need to assemble a million men in a given corner of the hemisphere, so gold served for her excuse. Later on she will supply them with industrial activities by way of compensation.

The future source of wealth in California will be agriculture and commerce; the search of gold, like all manual labor, will nourish man, and that is all. That is why there is so much disillusionment in store for those who go out to San Francisco, so much discouragement among those who return. San Francisco, and by San Francisco is meant all of New California, is just emerging from this reign of chaos and is on the point of realizing the rôle for which she was born. The spirit of the Lord is already afloat on the waters, but his lamp has not yet been lit.

INDEX

INDEX

S Clara Co ?,